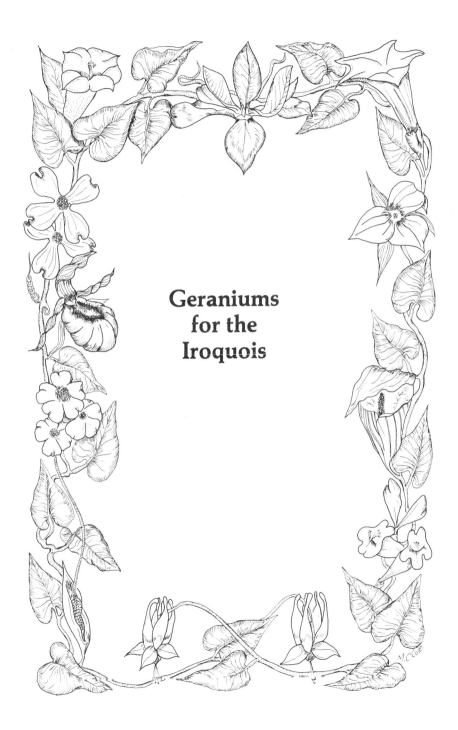

# Geraniums
# for the
# Iroquois

# GERANIUMS FOR THE IROQUOIS

## A FIELD GUIDE TO AMERICAN INDIAN MEDICINAL PLANTS

Daniel E. Moerman

Illustrations by
Marie Cole

REFERENCE PUBLICATIONS, INC.

Published January 1982

Printed in the United States of America

Library of Congress Cataloging in Publication Data

Moerman, Daniel E.
    Geraniums for the Iroquois.

    Bibliography: p.
    Includes index.
    1. Indians of North America—Medicine.
    2. Ethnobotany—North America. Materia medica,
Vegetable—North America.   I. Title.
E98.M4M68        615'.321        81-52514
ISBNN 0-917256-15-8              AACR2
ISBN 0-917256-17-4 (pbk.)

*Library of Congress Catalog Card Number: 81-52514*
*International Standard Book Number 0-917256-17-4*

Reference Publications, Inc.
218 St. Clair River Drive, Box 344
Algonac, Michigan 48001

# Dedication

For Marquisa and Jennifer,
with love

# Acknowledgements

This book has been a long time brewing, and many people have contributed to the work on which it is based. To the people of St. Helena Island in South Carolina who first taught me about healing plants over a decade ago, I owe my profound thanks; they changed my life. The staff of the University of Michigan-Dearborn Library, particularly Shirley Smith, worked with me for years with humor and imagination gathering the (incredibly scattered) published literature on native American healing. Bob Brill of the University of Michigan Computing Center was instrumental in helping me to organize these data in a useable fashion; if anyone has ever made computers work for people (rather than the reverse) it is he. I also appreciate a summer fellowship from the National Endowment for the Humanities which allowed me to organize the material fully.

The poem by Emily Dickinson, quoted on page 155, is reprinted by permission of the publishers from *The Poems of Emily Dickinson*, edited by Thomas H. Johnson, Cambridge, Massachusetts; Harvard University Press. Copyright 1951, 1955, 1979, by the President and Fellows of Harvard College.

Keith Irvine suggested this project and supported it in many ways, personal and otherwise. Marie Cole, whose illustrations grace these pages, has my deepest thanks—she tolerated my ambiguity and impatience with gracious ease. She particularly wants to thank Dr. Edward Voss of the University of Michigan Herbarium who offered helpful counsel on taxonomy.

Others who provided moral or actual support include B. Holly Smith, Lawrence Radine, and Jennifer Moerman. During most of the time that I was writing this book, Marquisa Moerman was involved in a *much* more complicated project of her own; her steadfast support, therefore, is all the more appreciated.

My ultimate thanks, of course, go to those generations of unknown native Americans whose passionate concern for the life and well-being of their kinsmen and friends led them to gather the human knowledge which I report here. We are all in their debt.

Ann Arbor, Michigan                                    **D.M.**
August, 1981

# Contents

# CONTENTS

ESKIMO

ALEUT

TLINGIT
TSIMSHIAN
GITSKAN
BELLA COOLA
CARRIER
THOMPSON INDIANS
KWAKIUTL
NOOTKA

BLACKFOOT

MONTAGNAIS

MICMAC
PENOBSCOT
OJIBWA
CHIPPEWA
IROQUOIS
MENOMINEE
FOX
MOHEGAN
SHOSHONE
TETON  OMAHA
WINNEBAGO
PAWNEE
POTAWATOMI
NANTICOKE
DELAWARE

PAIUTE
WASHOE
YOKUTS

CHEROKEE

HOPI
CHEYENNE

LUISEÑO
COAHUILLA
PIMA
NAVAJO
TEWA
PAPAGO
ZUNI
CREEK
NATCHEZ
CHOCTAW

APACHE

AZTEC

# Introduction

In the beginning, according to an old Cherokee tale, birds, animals, fishes and insects could all talk, and they all lived together with humans in harmony. But people, inventing bows, knives, fish hooks, spears, and other weapons, began to hunt animals. The people increased in number and began to spread at the expense of the other creatures. The animals found themselves without sufficient room to live. Not only were larger animals hunted for their flesh and skins, but frogs and worms were trodden upon mercilessly, out of pure human carelessness. The animals, talking this matter over among themselves, decided to do something about it. The bears decided to try to kill humans with bows and arrows, but found that they couldn't shoot bows without cutting off their claws, which would have meant that they couldn't hunt; they would all starve. So they gave up the attempt and moved deeper into the forests of the Great Smoky Mountains.

Then all the deer held a meeting and decided that, if men said the proper prayer in order to ask the pardon of the deer for the offense, they might kill them. Any hunter who did not say the proper prayer would be stricken with painful rheumatism.

Similarly, the other animals, the birds, insects, squirrels and frogs, decided that the humans must be controlled. To do so, they invented a whole list of diseases which would kill people, and keep them in check. Indeed, they were so inventive in creating diseases, that mankind would surely have been completely destroyed.

At this point, the plants, who had no argument with people, heard about the initiative of the animals. They decided to thwart their evil intention. Each plant, each grass, tree, shrub, herb, even the mosses, agreed to provide a remedy for one of the diseases invented by the animals.

In this way, Cherokee medicine originated. The plants provide the remedies for the diseases of mankind: today, when a doctor is in doubt of what to do for a patient, the spirit of the appropriate plant will suggest the proper remedy in a dream.

Similar tales can be found in the mythical repertoire of many native American peoples. Plants are the source of powerful spiritual medical forces. They offer up their healing power in return only for respect, or for a small offering, often of tobacco or perhaps some beads, to be left at the site where the healing herb is collected.

What are we to make of such a situation? Whatever were they doing with all those plants? And what does this story about the animals have to do with anything? As an anthropologist, I approach a problem like this from a comparative perspective. Medicine is a universal human phenomenon; all peoples try to control illness and heal the sick. One way to learn about human healing is to compare these human healing ways, to find the common elements, and to try to understand them. I will argue that both elements, the plants and the story, worked together in native American medicine to produce a high-quality healing system which was well suited to the health problems these people faced. Moreover, I will further argue that the two dimensions of healing which the plants and the story represent are both present in our own — and indeed in *any* — medical system. To do this, I will first consider the medicinal value of plants, and second, the medicinal value of "story," or meaning.

### Plants as Medicine

In our culture, we do not think of plants as medicines; and we tend to think of medicines as pills, or perhaps injections. But what are those pills made of? Few any more are pure plant material, although one—digitalis for congestive heart disease—is still sometimes prescribed that way, as capsules of powdered leaves of the foxglove plant. But this is not because the plants are not medicinal, only because the drug plants contain varying concentrations of the specific active principles, or because they contain several active principles, and only one is useful for the specific disease. So pharmacologists extract certain desirable chemicals from the leaves or roots of plants, standardize quantities, and package them conveniently.

Hundreds of such drugs are well known in contemporary medicine. Ephedrine, for example, is derived from the Chinese horsetail and used for a variety of purposes, but is best known as a decongestant. Reserpine is an important drug used to combat high blood pressure; it is derived from the roots of the Indian snakeroot plant. Quinine, long the standard treatment for malaria, is derived from the bark of the Peruvian cinchona tree. Morphine, the standard medical painkiller or analgesic, is, of course, derived from the opium poppy. Podophyllin is a resin derived from the roots of May apples; it is used to treat vaginal warts. Several very potent hypnotic and analgesic chemicals—atropine, scopalomine, and hyoscamine—are derived from three closely related plants, nightshade, Jimsonweed, and mandrake. Some more humble medicines derived from plants would include "witch hazel" which is distilled from witch hazel tree bark, and menthol which is derived from peppermint.

That it is necessary to state that plants have medicinal value is an historical oddity. Indeed, in our culture 100 years ago, this was just ordinary "common knowledge," to be classed with the notions that the sky is blue, that the sun rises in the east. Certainly the vast mass of tribal peoples in this world would not argue the proposition. The common names of hundreds of plants, applied to them in the 18th or 19th centuries, or before, testify to this: pleurisy root, boneset, allheal, selfheal, snakeroot, canker lettuce, cough root, toothache tree, worm root, worm seed, wormwood, colic root; the list goes on and on.

That people are generally unaware of the medicinal values of plants is probably due to two things. First, many of our newer drugs in use today are not derived from plants, but from other sources. Many are synthetic substances which do not exist in nature as such, and many of our best known drugs, like antibiotics, are soil molds of one sort or another. But probably the major reason that people are unaware of plant drugs lies in the professionalization of medicine and pharmacy. In fact, many physicians do not know very much about the drugs they prescribe—they know that such and such a drug is said to be effective for a certain condition, so they prescribe it, not caring particularly where it comes from, or what it is.

The professionalization of knowledge is certainly a good thing. Without such specialization, there are many interesting and useful things we would lack, like penicillin and, say, concert violinists. But the price we pay for the incredible expansion of contemporary knowledge is, paradoxically, an increase in ignorance. If I spend 10 years studying medicinal plants, I must necessarily forego time I might otherwise spend learning about solar technology, real estate investment, nuclear fusion, or playing my violin. Moreover, if I decide to shift my interest to, perhaps, endocrinology, the technical consequences of professionalization would have created a serious obstacle for me: the terms and technology are by now so complex it would take years to figure out what was really going on. A person working on the frontiers of any scientific or humanistic field today might find two or three or ten people in the country with whom he could talk about what he was doing without having to fill in a lot of background. No wonder people don't know much about plant drugs!

In addition to this problem, there is another. Today, many people do not know very much about *plants* or botany. In tribal societies, knowledge of flora is often extensive and complex. The Navajo, for example, can recognize and name many hundreds of plant species which grow in the Southwest. This is, for them, "common knowledge," the kind of thing that "everyone knows," equivalent to American common knowledge which lets people name dozens of baseball or football teams, or list the names and "stars" of countless Hollywood movies, or recognize the makers, styles and ages of scores of automobiles. We are brought up in a world of, among other things, sports teams, movies, automobiles and other brand name products. Navajos are brought up in a world of, among other things, plants.

Perhaps the most poignant example of this difference is illustrated in the charming and classic novel *Return to Laughter*, where Eleanor Smith Bowen (pseudonym for the noted anthropologist Laura Bohannan) tells of her encounter with Kako's people, whom she had gone to live with in Africa. Her problems were daunting, but the paramount difficulty was that she could not speak their language. People tried to teach her by pointing to things and saying their names. Small children, trying to help, picked the simplest, most obvious objects for their language lessons, the plants around them. She could not learn the *names* for the plants because she *couldn't recognize the differences between the plants*:

> I stared at the leaves. I fingered the leaves, and drew the leaves... I confused corn with guinea corn and at least three, very similar, wild grasses. I couldn't and still can't, tell one kind of yam leaf from the next. The little boy, no more than eight years old, stood beside me and prompted me; he knew them all. He became politely bored, and promised we should try again some other, unspecified, time. Then he drew his toga more closely about him and withdrew... I was left with the leaves and my notebook and a strong regret that I hadn't chosen to study a people like the Bedouin who have camels and a desert, both readily identifiable.

The only place where a North American today is likely to learn the names of wild trees or plants is in the Boy or Girl Scouts, or similar organizations. Yet my (old) Boy Scout *Handbook* says that, for the Nature merit badge, the boy must identify 15 species of plants in a field or forest. There are, in North America, over 17,000 species of plants. Nowadays, someone other than a professional botanist who could walk through a copse of trees and name two dozen species would probably be considered quite an expert!

Not only were native American people conversant with hundreds of species of plants, they knew much about their medicinal properties. How did they discover these properties? We really do not know the answer to this question, but we can guess. They must have proceeded empirically, trying things out. For this effort, they had a long tradition to fall back on. People have been using medicinal plants for at least 60,000 years, since the time of the

Neanderthals. In that length of time, the untold thousands of times that an injury or illness of a loved one—a spouse or child or friend—has spurred someone to *try*, to attempt to reduce suffering or save a life, must have been successful on occasion. And people can talk, can remember, can distill the wisdom of their age as they teach their children. Knowledge of medicine is as old as mankind.

Many native American drugs were quickly adopted by immigrant Europeans, and vice-versa. But I am unaware of any North American medicinal plant that was not known to native Americans. In the 12,000 or 20,000 years that they lived here before the arrival of Europeans, they apparently found all of them!

### Meaning as Medicine

I noted earlier that native American medicine had two elements, the plants and the "story." Let us now consider stories. The myth about the origin of medicine which started this introduction is a good example. What it does for people who know and believe it is to give them confidence in their treatment and belief in the possibility of a cure by providing them with a *theory of medicine*, with the knowledge that the experience they are about to undergo (taking a drug) is a *meaningful* one.

Often, for native Americans as well as for many other peoples including Europeans, the meaning of a particular plant drug involved a similarity between the plant, or its leaves or roots, and the organ that it would treat. Known in its simpler forms as the "Doctrine of Signatures," this theory often suggested using yellow flowered plants for jaundice, red-sapped plants to stop bleeding, lobe-leafed plants for liver diseases, and so on.

There are more sophisticated versions of this approach to healing. The Iroquois, for example, have a highly complex theory of illness, and an equally complex theory of medical treatment which involves a series of principles regarding plants. For the Iroquois, illness was the tangible consequence of an imbalance of some sort in the patient's system.

This imbalance was deemed the result of one of four sorts of causes. First, localized but mild symptoms of discomfort, like sores or boils, were considered to result from the fact that an individual had violated a rule or taboo. Such rule violations might include neglecting the spirits of the dead, making mistakes in ritual, or not properly carrying out acts of contrition before hunting (compare this with the Cherokee theory mentioned earlier), and so on. Second, generalized but mild or vague symptoms, like longstanding chronic illnesses, depression or anxiety, and loneliness or homesickness, were the result of "unfulfilled desires." If such desires were truly unfulfillable, the patient was treated by purging to eliminate the "thing" inside him causing the problem.

A third kind of illness, which was generally understood to cause intense and painful but localized symptoms, was the result of coming into contact with various "evil powers" in the world, usually certain unpleasant animals or plants. Such illnesses were treated with (among other things) plants which were eaten by, or resembled, or somehow counteracted the evil powers. The fourth class of illnesses involved those with symptoms which were both generalized and intense or painful, like convulsions, insanity, paralysis, blindness, and so on, things which totally disrupted the person's life. Such illnesses were considered to be the results of deliberate witchcraft, and could only be alleviated by treatment with powerful and dangerous medicines. Among these were plants which were themselves considered to be the "evil powers" mentioned earlier.

An Iroqouis patient is suffering from sores on the mouth. Such an illness is presumed to be the consequence of violation of some rule or taboo (it is localized and mild). Perhaps the patient smoked someone else's pipe. Consulting a physician, he might be told to make a tea of the roots of the wild or spotted cranesbill, the wild geranium, *Geranium maculatum*, and wash the sore with this liquid several times a day. The wild geranium produces seeds which have large claw-like hooks. Along with other plants that have such ensnaring or capturing qualities, this is exactly the kind of thing that would be expected by the Iroquois to heal an open, everted, running illness, like a cold sore. Such knowledge would provide the confidence and motivation to continue the process (a sociologist might see this as a technique to enhance "patient compliance"). It would also add to the patient's peace of mind, reducing the stress and worry which accompanies illness and mitigates its cure. And, the roots of the wild geranium are rich

*WILD GERANIUM:* Geranium maculatum. *Wild geranium is a one to two-foot tall plant with large, five-lobed leaves. "Cranesbill" derives its name from the unusual, pointed seeds which develop after the fine rose-purple petals fall. This is a common plant of woods and shady roadsides.*

sources of the astringent tannin which is an excellent specific medication for drying up sores and wounds.

Both the plant itself and the knowledge and understanding of the plant combine to produce a reasonable and, probably, quite effective cure for a simple but very irritating illness. In such a case, the wild geranium is not only "good to use" on sores, but also "good to think" on sores.

Drugs are not only medicinal but also meaningful. Unfortunately, while we know a fair amount about the medicinal qualities of many plants used by native Americans, we know a good deal less about what they mean to them. This is in part due to the fact that while the tannin content of wild geranium is necessarily the same for the Iroquois, the Chippewa and us, the meaning is not! Just as different cultures speak different languages, they "prescribe different (botanical or medical) languages." Thus, if I (not an Iroquois) went to the doctor with a sore on my lip, he might tell me that I had "primary acute herpetic gingivostomatitis," and that it was the result of a local injury or more general stress activating a quiescent infection of *Herpes simplex*, a virus which I probably first contracted as an infant. Suppose at this point he told me that I might go and find some wild geranium roots and chew them. This is, of course, as unlikely as if, half way through the office visit, he stopped speaking English and began speaking Iroquois! But, just suppose. I am sure that I would become quite upset. For, as an American born and bred, this just *isn't right*. It doesn't *matter* about the tannin content of geranium roots. I don't have a theory of hook-like ensnaring qualities in medicine for sores. Such an experience, for most North Americans, just wouldn't *feel* right, and would probably aggravate rather than soothe the situation. In our culture, it seems most reasonable to treat such an illness with an ointment. Our idea generally is that wounds should be *covered*, to protect them from "germs," or from "bad air." We have, of course, a long history of concern with the air; we all "know," for example, that one can "catch a cold" from sitting in a "draft."

Since one can rarely bandage a sore on a lip to protect it from air, the next best thing is an ointment, preferably with an oil base. So, what is much more likely is that my physician will write some words in a secret code on a piece of paper. I will take the paper to another professional (similarly dressed in a white coat) who, in addition to selling liquor, newspapers, hardware and outdoor furniture, has been trained to decode the secret message; he will sell me a petroleum based ointment containing some astringent and a mild anesthetic. This scenario, so much more "right" for us than the wild geranium cure, is probably no more or less effective. In terms of the comparative anthropological perspective mentioned earlier, the two cures contain precisely comparable elements; an anthropologist would say that the two situations are "structurally identical"—they contain the same kinds of elements—even though there are modest (or, in other cases, perhaps major) differences in content. Such meaningful behavior is always part of the human medical process, in greater or lesser part depending on various cultural or biological circumstances.

Such appropriately meaningful behavior can strongly influence human biology. Let me note from the start that it is about here where I get into trouble with this argument, where the serious controversy begins. I usually have only a little difficulty convincing people that plants have medicinal value. It is usually not too difficult for people of our culture to recognize the meaningful qualities of medical treatments, the syntax of medicine. In fact, many people are quite clear in their preferences among the many varieties of certain drugs—"Brand X works much better for me than Brand Z"—even when all the brands contain the same active ingredients. But when I state that this meaningful aspect of medicine is *biologically active*, the going begins to get rough. I generally argue that medicine has a meaningful cultural content as well as a biochemical effect. Certain things "go together." There are, in any society, certain "right" and "wrong" ways to heal the sick. These meaningful aspects of medicine can have a profound effect on the healing process. The study of this fascinating topic has only just begun and it is just beginning to add up. I will cite a little bit of the evidence here to give you a taste of it. Much of this evidence comes from medical research which has employed "placebos."

Placebos are inert medical treatments, that is, pills or injections of substances which, in themselves, have no effect on human biology. Placebo pills are usually made of starch or chalk. Placebo injections are usually saline solution, that is, salt water. Researchers often test drugs by randomly dividing a group of patients into two groups, and then giving one group the new drug and the other group a matching placebo. When the drug group does much better than the placebo group, the drug is considered to be chemically effective. Many such studies have been done.

A remarkable thing about these studies is the response to the placebos. A large proportion of patients can be treated effectively with inert drugs! Consider a study of ulcer patients done several years ago in France. Several physicians worked together in a study of drugs which, it was thought, might speed the healing of ulcers. One group of patients received no treatment at all—they were told only to limit their smoking, avoid aspirin, and were counselled on their diets. For these 30 patients, ulcer pain lasted for an average of 20 days. Several other groups of patients, given the same advice, were also given drugs or matching placebos. The drugs were not shown to be more effective than the placebos. But the placebo patients responded much better than the untreated patients; their pain lasted for an average of only 7 days. Even more remarkable was the fact that the patients showed substantial differences in how long the pain lasted depending on which physician they had. One doctor's patients experienced an average of 12 days of pain, another's 7 days, another's 6.5 days, and another's 3.5 days; recall that all these patients were treated with placebos!

Many other studies have shown unusual things about placebos. It has been shown, for example, that two placebos are more effective than one; it has been shown that patients treated with three different-looking placebos—two weeks each—responded better than patients treated with the same placebo for six weeks. The colors of placebo pills are important to their effects. In a curious experiment in England, a group of medical students was told they were going to test pills which were either tranquilizers or stimulants. They were each given one or two pink or blue placebo tablets. The students who took blue tablets reported that they got very sleepy while the ones who took the pink tablets reported that they felt high, stimulated. Students who took two tablets reported stronger reactions than those who took only one. One student responded so strongly to two blue tablets that he had to be admitted to the University clinic with a case of severe depression.

Placebos have been shown to relieve the symptoms of a wide range of illnesses—angina, hypertension, ulcers, seasickness, pain, and so on. In general, the only illnesses which are resistant to placebo treatment are resistant to *all* treatment.

In our own contemporary medicine, we have a series of ideas about what makes medicine "work." Various treatments have various amounts of "power" associated with them. Generally, shots are more powerful than pills; colored pills are more powerful than white ones. Large pills (containing a lot of medicine) and very tiny pills (containing very concentrated medicine) are more powerful than medium sized pills. Capsules are more powerful than tablets, and multicolored capsules are more powerful than single colored capsules. Medicines that have to be kept in the refrigerator are more powerful than medicines that can be kept in the bathroom medicine chest. More expensive medicines are more powerful than cheap medicines. Liquid medicines should be red or pink but not green or blue. Ointments should look like petroleum jelly, and should *not* be colorful, while antiseptics should be blood colored. Prescribed medicines are more powerful than over-the-counter medicines (medical books frequently recommend that, when the appropriate drug for an illness is not a prescription drug, the physician should prescribe it anyway—with his prescription pad—to convince the patient of its efficacy).

There is no scientific evidence for any of these ideas, but they *are* our ideas. As such, it seems reasonable to believe that they are, in another sense, true. Placebo effectiveness is a function of what people believe about things.

I do not mean to indicate by this discussion of placebos that *drugs* are not chemically effective, far from it. Likewise, I do not mean to indicate that the drugs of American Indians, or plant drugs generally, are effective only because they are placebos; these plants do have chemically active ingredients. I do mean to indicate that medicine has two kinds of effectiveness which both operate simultaneously.

I think of these two dimensions of effectiveness as "specific" and "general." The specific effectiveness of aspirin resides in its contents of acetylsalicylic acid which is an excellent analgesic (no one is quite sure why). The general effectiveness of aspirin lies in the fact that it is a *pill* which is the "kind of thing" that people know to be analgesics, and little white pills are quite effective pain killers (no one is quite sure why). The general effectiveness of, say, Cherokee medicines lies in part in the myth which opened this chapter—people *know* that the plants have vowed to help them fight diseases. Cherokees know, for example, that if someone has a cold and fever, he should drink some willow bark tea. General effectiveness lies in the Cherokee knowledge that willows protect people against fevers. Specific effectiveness resides in the salicin content of willow bark (salicin is a naturally occurring chemical similar to aspirin found in most willow species—the chemical is named after the genus of the willows, *Salix*).

The study of general medical effectiveness is in its infancy. What precisely differentiates those four French physicians mentioned earlier is, I'm afraid, anyone's guess. The color of pills is, to date, a marketing decision, not a medical one. Further on in this book you will meet some of the knowledge and skill which native American peoples brought to this problem. Perhaps some day we will have equivalent knowledge of our own which will extend and augment our own healing processes by design rather than simply by chance.

### A Note on Taking Drugs

This book is *not* a medical guide. An old homily of the bar says "A lawyer who defends himself has a fool for a client. "Much the same might be said for physicians, and for would-be physicians: "A patient who treats himself has a fool for a doctor."

This is not to say that anyone's health is the responsibility of anyone else. It is to say that a responsible person guards his health with whatever steps are necessary and appropriate, and often this requires competent professional help. This book is written in the conviction that native Americans were acute observers of nature, competent botanists, superb psychiatrists, and excellent physicians. But, much more important, it is written in the certain knowledge that pre-Columbian Americans were vastly more healthy than Europeans of that time, or even Euro-Americans of our time. This is a simple consequence of demography—not of medicine, or physical vigor. Living in small and relatively isolated communities, and without significant numbers of domesticated animals (source and reservoir of an appalling number of human diseases), native Americans simply did not create the conditions for the evolution and adaptation of diseases that Europeans did. Native American medicine did not have to deal with epidemic diseases (plague, typhoid, cholera, measles, tuberculosis), with cancer, or (in all likelihood) with cardio-vascular diseases as we know them. It did deal with psychological, rheumatic, urinary, and gastro-intestinal problems, and with rashes, fractures, wounds and irritations (especially of the eyes—largely from living in smoky houses). These medical problems were treated seriously. Practitioners served long apprenticeships. Medicine, hunting or horticulture, and religion were usually meshed together in a complex whole which I violate merely by listing these "elements" separately. It is in this context that, to paraphrase the great anthropologist Claude Levi-Strauss, some plants are good to eat, but some are good to think. This book is written in the spirit of that remark.

I have not tried all of the drugs discussed in this book. Indeed, had I been so sick in so many ways, I should have died long before the book was written! Generally, I do not recommend that anyone should take any of them. What then is the purpose? Does a bird-watcher, seeing a pileated woodpecker or a warbler in the spring, have to shoot, pluck, cook, and eat it in order to derive satisfaction from his experience? Certainly not! The same is true of plants, and particularly medicinal plants. Some plants are "good to think." Some of them are particularly "good to think" if you have specimens in your garden, or as a target for your camera.

Further on you will find several discussions of plants which native Americans used as sedatives or tranquilizers to reduce nervous tension. Suppose you are nervous and tense. You could take a Valium tablet, or you could brew and drink some *Humulus* tea. But there is another way. Put on some comfortable jeans and a pair of old boots. Take your field guide and some binoculars. Go to the country, or a wild park, or the unmowed edge of a highway. Spend an hour wandering about looking for some fresh *Humulus*. See what other plants are in bloom, or in seed, or still standing in the snow. Watch the birds; observe what they are eating. Watch the butterflies on the flowers. Look for Monarch butterfly larvae feeding on the milkweeds. Perhaps you will find some *Humulus.* Perhaps not. But thinking about and looking for *Humulus* is as good for nervous tension as drinking it. Go home. Get a good night's sleep. This will not relieve the conditions that caused your nervous tension (neither will Valium). But the tension will be relieved.

If you go to the hospital, people will send flowers (some of them may even be medicinal ones!). But you can beat them to the punch. Walk in the fields, meet the flowers on their own terms, learn their names, smell them. Ski over the same field in February. Shout "Hello!" to them under the snow. On a hot summer day, seek out some soothing calamus along a river. And remember Emerson's words: "We see the foaming brook with compunction: If our own life flowed with the right energy, we should shame the brook." The seeking out of herbal medicines is at least as valuable for health as is gathering them.

**About the information in this book.**

*The plants.*

All the plants considered in this book were used medicinally by native American peoples from Mexico to the Arctic. Not all of them are indigenous plant species. Immigrant Europeans brought their own medicinal plants with them to the New World, either deliberately or accidentally, whereupon many of them were adopted by native peoples. We have illustrated 75 species and discussed that many more. This, however, is but a tiny fraction, perhaps 10%, of the plants used medicinally by native Americans. How was this sample selected? I have included species which are widespread in nature, or which were widely used by many tribes, or which were subsequently adopted by Euro-American medicine, or which are particularly lovely, or particularly interesting, or some combination of these characteristics.

*Pharmacopeias.*

One bit of information often included in the discussion of the individual plants is their status in the "USP" and the "NF." The USP is the common designation of the United States Pharmacopeia. A pharmacopeia is a list of drugs and their standard formulations. As medicine and pharmacy became more professionalized in the 18th and 19th centuries, the two professions began to diverge. Before this (and to a lesser degree afterwards) physicians had acted as their own pharmacists, formulating drugs for their patients. But as specialists took up the job of formulating drugs, a communication problem of sorts appeared. Without a standard form of communication, a doctor could not know exactly how a pharmacist would formulate the drug he prescribed. Pharmacopeias were established, first in England in the 18th century, to solve this problem.

The first American pharmacopeia was written in 1820. A convention of physicians from the various regions of the country met in Washington, D.C. on January 1 of that year to collate suggestions made by several regional conventions. The first USP, published in December of 1820, listed 217 drugs considered useful, with standard doses, strengths, and formulas, printed in both English and Latin. For 150 years, this convention reconvened every ten years to revise the Pharmacopeias. New drugs were added, and old, presumably less effective, remedies were deleted. Since 1970, the Convention has met every five years.

In 1888, the American Pharmaceutical Association began publication of the National Formulary, the NF, to list drugs which were deemed effective but which were not listed in the USP, or which had been dropped from it. Thus, Serpentaria, the ground root of *Aristolochia serpentaria*, or snake root, which had been listed in the USP as a stimulant and tonic from 1820 was dropped in 1942. It was subsequently listed in the NF from 1942 until 1955. The pharmacopeias are an excellent source of information on the historical uses of drugs, reflecting the discovery of new herbal medicines and their subsequent replacement in therapy by newer, stronger, or more specific synthetic remedies.

*Illustrations and Range Maps.*

The illustrations in this book were drawn from living specimens or, following standard botanical practice, from dried specimens in the Herbarium of the University of Michigan. For most of the drawings, the decisive characteristics differentiating the species from similar ones are included, although this is not always possible.

The range maps, gathered together at the end of the book, illustrate the general ranges of the plants in continental terms.

Many species may be found only in particular habitats (in bogs, or in deep woods) within the listed range. The habitats are described in the text below the illustrations. These range maps are, therefore, only approximate; they can tell you if the plant exists in your part of the country, but not exactly where to find it.

*SMOOTH ASTER:* Aster laevis. *The smooth aster grows from one to three feet tall, and has a smooth stem clasped at the top by bluntly-based leaves. The lower leaves are narrower, tapered, and slightly toothed. The flowers have a yellow center surrounded by white or violet rays. Asters, which flower in the late summer, are distinctive plants of dry, open fields.*

## Asters, the "Michaelmas Daisies "

### *Aster laevis*

Asters are one of our most common wildflowers. They are also among the most lovely. They are among the most difficult to identify because there are so *many* of them. There are, depending on who is counting, approximately 120 different species of asters in North America; most states or provinces will have between 20 and 30 native species. Asters are members of the gigantic sunflower family with nearly 300 genera and over 2,000 species in North America alone. Some of the members of the family considered elsewhere in this book include dandelions, yarrow, and wormwood.

The sunflower family is characterized by having multiple or "composite" flowers. What look from a distance like "petals" are not petals at all, but modified leaves called "bracts." Each "flower" is really a collection of from two or three up to several hundred tiny separate flowers, called florets. Each floret produces one seed. Nothing is more fascinating than to grow a bunch of sunflowers or asters, and to closely examine with a magnifying glass the anatomy of the flowers as they open, and produce their pollen and seeds. Particularly fascinating is the patterns formed by the seeds in the mature flower; elegant expanding spirals form a magnificent pinwheel. Go look at some, you will see what I mean.

This profusion of aster species is well represented in their medicinal use by native Americans. At least 20 different species were used by 15 or 20 different groups, each group using a few favored local species. Since the classification of asters is complicated, it is often hard to know exactly which species a particular group was using. These species were used in a multitude of ways, and so it also is very difficult to evaluate their merit. I have elected to illustrate one of the most widespread species, the smooth aster, *Aster laevis*. The Fox Indians put the smooth aster on the hot rocks of their steam baths to furnish an invigorating steam. They had another use for the plant which is quite unusual. When someone was so sick that he had lost consciousness, a paper or bark cone was placed over his nostrils. Then the dried smooth aster plant was burned so the smoke was funnelled up the tube. Breathing the smoke would revive the patient. They used several other species of aster in the same way.

The Hopi likewise considered asters to be stimulants. A boiled tea of leaves and flowers was considered to be a particularly strong stimulating drink. The Hopi used several species of aster for other purposes as well. Aster root tea was used as a cold remedy; several species were made into boiled teas for anything which ailed pregnant women; aster root was added to many other medicines to strengthen them.

Several tribes—the Navajo, Mohegan, and Thompson Indians among them—used aster leaf or flower teas for stomach aches. The Navajo also ground the dried root or leaves to a fine powder and used it as a "snuff" to clear a congested head. The Zuni sprinkled the dried powdered leaves on abrasions, and used boiled leaf tea to wash bullet or arrow wounds.

The Iroquois, in addition to making several teas for reducing fevers, used the ground roots of asters as part of a rather complicated love medicine. There may be some kind of symbolic symmetry in the fact that aster root was part of another complex compound used to cure ven     disease.

The Iroquois were in widespread company in this last use. The Thompson Indians recommended a strong boiled tea for venereal diseases. The Roman Pliny likewise considered the aster to be effective in curing diseases of the groin; he wrote that one had to pick the flowers with the left hand and tie them on one's girdle as an amulet. He notes that this was also an effective remedy for sciatica!

The asters were never an important part of Western medicine; they were never official, and were rarely used. They now belong in the garden where their great virtue is that they flower late in the season after most of the rest of the blooms are gone. It is because of this habit that the asters are known in England as Michaelmas Daisies (Michaelmas falls on September 29). They are sturdy, hardy plants, most of them perennial; some of them retain their flowers even after covered with the first snows of October or November. Dozens of magnificent horticultural varieties are available from seed merchants, but one should recall that each state or province can be expected to have 20 or 30 wild native species. As you drive along country roads or walk through the fall woods, keep alert for the tiny blue star-flowers. Dig up a few and take them home for replanting. They are tough enough to withstand such rough treatment.

Only one legitimate medical use remains for these flowers today. The Potawatomi collected dried aster flowers and burned them like incense to repel evil spirits. The flowers should be dry and ready for picking by Halloween, when they are most needed.

*BALSAM FIR:* Abies balsamea. *The Balsam fir is readily recognized by its single, flat one-and-a-half inch long needles. The needles are slightly notched at the tips, and have two silvery bands on the undersides. The narrow, upright cones are two to four inches long. Resin blisters appear on the bark of the young firs. These 40 to 60-foot trees grow in moist soils.*

## Balsam.

### *Abies balsama*

The use of pitch, resin, sap and balsam, essentially substances which ooze out of trees, for healing "balms" on wounds or sores has an ancient lineage. Wars were fought in classical times over the control of the trade in myrrh, a gum resin from an Arabian tree.

In America, one of the most widely used resins is balsam, derived from several species of the genus *Abies*. The pitch of the balsam fir, *Abies balsamea*, was widely used by northeastern tribes as a salve for cuts and sores: the Potawatomi, Ojibwa, Iroquois, and Penobscot all used it in this way. In addition, the Menominee used the inner bark of the tree as a dressing or poultice for sores and cuts. The Carrier Indians of British Columbia used the sap on cuts but found it particularly useful for burns.

In the southwest, the Paiute, Shoshone, and some pueblo groups, notably the Tewa, used the pitch of the white fir, *Abies concolor*, for the same purposes. Although I am unaware of any direct evidence on the point, it seems quite probable that balsam has antibiotic properties, and plays much the same role in wound management as does our contemporary use of iodine or mercurochrome. Although these perparations are much more convenient, were you in the woods without a proper first aid kit with a wound in danger of infection, you should certainly use balsam if any is to be had. The large shiny blisters are easily plucked off the trunk of the fir, and the viscous fliud inside squeezed onto your wound.

Such external uses were many among native Americans, but hardly exhausted the pharmacy of balsam. It was also used both as a cold remedy and for bronchial diseases. The Potawatomi, Ojibwa, and Menominee ate balsam gum for colds, while the Blackfoot rubbed the gum on the chest for colds. Similarly, the Paiute and Washoe in Nevada ate the resin of the white fir for tuberculosis, while they, as well as the Shoshone, drank a tea of the bark or a boiled tea of the needles for any serious chest congestion. The Menominee used a similar bark tea from balsam fir for chest pain. The Bella Coola of British Columbia did the same, using the local species grand fir, *Abies grandis.*

Balsam was widely used in American medicine for similar bronchial and chest diseases throughout the 18th and 19th centuries. It probably has expectorant properties similar to those of the pine resins (see our chapter on Pines).

Nowadays, medicine has no particular use for balsam. The sticky fluid is used to mount microscope slides, firmly holding specimens in a clear, permanent matrix. It is also used to cement lenses together in magnifier optics. But is seems unlikely that anyone will fight a war over it. Thank goodness. The tall waving firs can continue to exude their healing antibiotic balsam in peace, for us to use on our cuts and bruises, and to chew for chest colds.

## Beardtongues, the best kept secret.

### *Penstemon grandiflorus*

It is a puzzle. One of the first things Europeans did when they came to the New World was to study plants and their medicinal uses by native Americans. Their success in that activity should be apparent in this book as so many plants used medicinally by the Indians became important parts of western medicine. The penstemons, however, never became part of the western pharmacopeia. As far as I can tell, they have never been closely examined for their medical character. Most writers on native American medicine ignore them completely. Yet at least 8 or 10 species were used medicinally by as many native American groups for a wide variety of purposes. Their medical "lineage" is a good one as they are in the snapdragon family along with the foxgloves, *Digitalis*, and Culver's root, *Veronicastrum virginicum*, two important medical species. They certainly did not escape the notice of the gardeners, as some of the more showy species (and, oh, how showy they can be!) were introduced to European gardens as early as the 1790s.

Part of the problem may be the complexity of the genus. There are approximately 140 species in North America, most of them with rather small ranges, many of them very difficult to tell apart, even by specialists. The diversity of species is greatest in the west—California has over 50 species, and the northern Rocky Mountain region has several dozen. In the east and south most areas will have 6 to 8 species. The most widespread species, the foxglove beardtongue, *Penstemon digitalis*, is found everywhere east of the Rockies and south of Hudson's Bay, but apparently was not used medicinally by native Americans.

The group which used the penstemons the most was the Navajo. They used several different species. The root of *P. barbatus* was ground to a powder which was dusted on burns; also a root tea was used to wash burns. The boiled root was also taken as a cough medicine, for stomach aches, and for menstrual cramps. Another species, *P. jamesii*, was used along with several other plants in a tea taken to relieve headaches. A boiled tea of the root of another

*BEARDTONGUE:* Penstemon grandiflorus. *Beardtongue was named for the tufted male flower parts (stamens) which are found in the throats of the large, lavender-blue, tubular flowers. The leaves are arranged opposite one another on smooth stems. These two to four-foot plants grow several stems per clump. Found in dry prairies, this species flowers in May and June.*

species, *P. linarioides*, was taken by women to ease labor and childbirth.

Other tribes also used various beardtongues for a variety of purposes. The Thompson Indians, Blackfoot, Cherokee, Paiute, and Shoshone, like the Navajo, used boiled teas of the roots of various species for cramps and stomach aches. The Thompson Indians, Paiute and Tewa used various species on cuts and wounds; the Thompson Indians, for example, toasted and crumbled the stems and leaves of *P. heterodoxus* and then sprinkled the powder on sores, cuts and wounds.

The Pawnee used a boiled leaf tea of the large-flowered penstemon, *P. grandiflorus*, for chills and fever, while the Natchez used a boiled root tea of another species for colds and coughs.

It is difficult to recommend that anyone should use the penstemons medicinally. First, the problem of identification is serious; one would have to be *very* expert to be sure of exactly which species he had. Second, the uses discussed, except for the apparent consensus on stomach aches and cramps, are so diffuse that no clear pattern is evident. It is, however, easy to recommend them for your garden! Some of the horticultural varieties are absolutely stunning flowers with intensely deep reds, blues and particularly purples. And many of the wild species are similarly beautiful. Many of them grow only a few inches high in dense low mounds completely covered with brilliant deep-hued blooms. The loveliest ones I have seen were in the mountains of northern Colorado and southern Wyoming; no other wild flowers I have ever seen have had equally deep, intense, velvety colors. They make excellent border plants, around the taller herbs in your garden.

But, perhaps we should all agree to keep the secret. After 300 or 400 years, we have ample precedent. I won't tell if you don't.

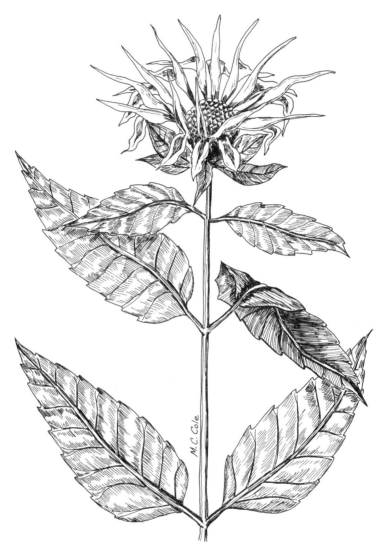

*BEEBALM:* Monarda fistulosa. *Beebalm, a square-stemmed member of the mint family, is readily recognized by its showy head of tubular, lilac or pale pink flowers. The toothed, tapering leaves of the 2 to 3 foot tall plants are paired on the stem. Found in clearings, thickets and wood borders, beebalm flowers in July and August.*

## Beebalm and Thyme: Fragrant antiseptics.

### *Monarda fistulosa*

Beebalm or horsemint, *Monarda fistulosa,* is one of several indigenous American species of this genus of the mint family which was commonly used medicinally by American Indians. Thyme, *Thymus vulgaris,* is a European member of the mint family which has been long in use medicinally in the Old World. Both plants are sources of thymol, a common drug in Western medicine with antibacterial, antifungal, and anthelmintic properties.

The most common use of beebalm by native Americans was as a treatment for headaches and fevers. The Teton Sioux drank boiled blossom tea for fevers while the Tewa ate the ground leaves and also used them as a poultice on the head. Both the Iroquois and Cherokee also used beebalm for headaches. Other tribes used closely related species; the Fox, for example, used a snuff of ground leaves of horsemint, *Monarda punctata,* for headaches. The Navajo used beebalm, *M. pectinata,* in a tea which was washed over and drunk by a feverish patient.

The Fox, Navajo, Sioux, and Nanticoke used various species of Monarda for cold remedies, usually in the form of boiled teas. The Blackfoot made an eyewash of beebalm blossoms while the Chippewa used beebalm roots and blossoms in a boiled tea for intestinal parasites.

Several tribes used *Monarda fistulosa* for wounds or other skin diseases. The Winnebago, for instance, used boiled leaf tea as a cleansing bath for acne. And the name of the plant comes from the universal use of the plant as a treatment for insect bites: rubbing the crumbled leaves on bites quickly reduces pain or itching.

During classical times, our other major source of thymol, the common thyme, *Thymus vulgaris,* was a very important plant. Our name for it comes from the Greek name *thymon,* which apparently indicated its use as incense, coming from the Greek *thyein,* meaning to burn as a sacrifice. The Romans considered it a helpful stimulant and remedy for illnesses of the spleen. During the 16th century, the herbalists recommended it as a stimulant, to reduce fevers, and to heal insect bites, either taken internally or applied directly.

An American beebalm, *Monarda punctata,* was in the USP from 1820 until 1882, recommended as a stimulant and carminative, essentially an aid to digestion. From 1882 until the present day, thymol has been listed in the USP, recommended originally as an anthelmintic (especially good for hookworms), and antiseptic; today it is found in a number of patent medicines, notably Vicks Vapo-rub.

Contemporary uses of thyme are legion, but they are largely confined to the kitchen where the herb is one of the classic French flavorings along with parsley, tarragon, and bay leaves. Its pungent aroma enhances salads, eggs, fish and vegetables. Beebalm likewise now belongs more to the culinary than the medicinal arts and beebalm tea is a   refreshing and stimulating change from ordinary coffee or black tea. And the possibility always remains for you to substitute beebalm for thyme in your sacrifices.

## Black Birch and Wintergreen.

### *Betula lenta*

### *Gaultheria procumbens*

It may seem strange to consider together two such different plants as the black or sweet birch, a towering tree growing to 60 feet, and the inconspicuous trailing wintergreen, or teaberry, often only two inches tall! But there is a good reason.

Birches, black birch among them, had several medicinal uses for native Americans. Three different groups used boiled teas of various birch species for stomach aches and cramps: the Western Eskimo used *Betula nana*, the Chippewa used river birch, *B. nigra*, while the Ojibwa used white birch, *B. papyrifera*.

The Potawatomi added birch twig tea to other medicines as a strengthener, while the Creek used the bark in a medicine for tuberculosis. The Cherokee used a tea of black birch, *B. lenta*, or river birch bark for dysentery, colds, and stomach ailments. The Iroquois used a boiled tea of black birch for venereal diseases, colds, and for fever and soreness, that is, for flu symptoms. The Iroquois considered the black birch to be a particularly useful medicine since the tree sustained the deer.

The lovely wintergreen, *Gaultheria procumbens*, with its pink-tinged white nodding bell flowers, found its greatest medicinal use as an antirheumatic. The Delaware, Menominee, Ojibwa, Potawatomi, and Iroquois all used the leaves in one way or another (usually in a boiled tea) for aching, rheumatic joints. The Bella Coola of British Columbia sprinkled the powdered toasted leaves on cuts as an antiseptic. Both the Delaware and Iroquois used the leaves in a tea as a general tonic. The Potawatomi used a boiled leaf tea to reduce fevers.

Wintergreen, in one form or another, has been listed in the USP from 1820 to the present day. It was the primary source of oil of wintergreen, which has as its major constituent the chemical methyl salicylate. Distilled birch twigs yield an oil which has essentially the same qualities as wintergreen oil. When this was

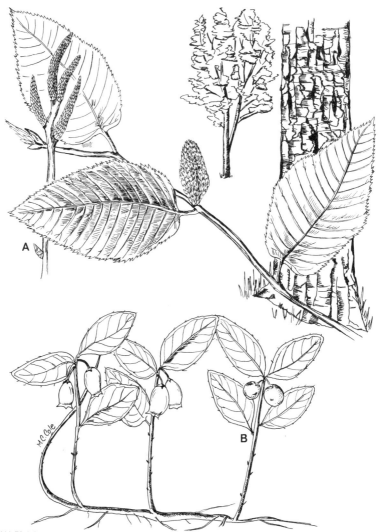

**(A)** *BLACK BIRCH:* Betula lenta. *The mature, bright green, double-toothed leaves of the Black Birch are arranged alternately on wintergreen flavored twigs. Older trees, found in rich woods, have dark brown, furrowed, plate-like bark.*

**(B)** *WINTERGREEN:* Gaultheria procumbens. *The fragrant leaves of the two to five-inch tall wintergreen are characteristically evergreen. The upright branches arise from creeping stems. Spicy, dry, red berries develop from the pinkish flowers which bloom in late summer. Clearings or open woods.*

discovered in the 1850s, birch was added to the USP. Today, the official substance listed in the pharmacopoeia is methyl salicylate, a very close chemical relative of aspirin (acetylsalicylic acid), with a number of similar properties. It can be made by distillation of either plant, or it can be produced synthetically; most methyl salicylate in use today is synthetic (made by esterification of synthetic salicylic acid with methyl alcohol). It is used topically in liniments and ointments as a counterirritant for rheumatic conditions, lumbago and sciatica. It is also used in minute quantities as a flavoring agent in medicines. Formerly, it was used internally in much the way we now use aspirin, to stop pain and reduce fevers and inflammation.

Aspirin is a much better drug for these purposes than methyl salicylate for one very good reason. While aspirin is a toxic substance which is potentially poisonous, it is not nearly so poisonous as methyl salicylate. The minimum fatal dose of methyl salicylate is as little as four milliliters for a child, six for an adult. Four milliliters is about one small drop from an eyedropper. Generally speaking then, one should avoid wintergreen oil like the plague.

Wintergreen leaves, collected in the fall and made into a mild tea by pouring hot water on them for a few moments, make a soothing tea—just the thing for sore aching muscles on a long fall hike, or after a day of canoeing with two or three portages. Black birch twigs, smashed between a few rocks, will make a similar tea. During the American Revolution, when Chinese tea, *Camellia sinensis*, was unavailable, wintergreen was an acceptable substitute. In certain contexts it still is today.

*BLOODROOT:* Sanguinaria canadensis. *The most characteristic feature of this early spring wild flower is the orange-red juice of the broken stem. The lobed leaves are six to twelve inches wide. A leafless stalk bears white flowers with eight to ten petals. Rootstalks are half to one inch thick, and several inches long, with fibrous roots. Found in rich woods.*

## Bloodroot

### *Sanguinaria canadensis*

The Delaware Indians were among the most enthusiastic native American users of bloodroot. They would eat a small piece of the root daily, much as you or I might take a vitamin pill, just for general good health. They also used the root in a compound with several other herbs as a general strengthener for women—it was thought to enhance sexual vitality. They used it as well as a blood "purifier," and for stomach aches.

The Fox and Menominee added bloodroot to other medicines to strengthen them; the Fox used the boiled root as a burn dressing. The Potawatomi used bloodroot tea as a sore throat remedy. They also "sugar coated the pill"—they squeezed the root juice on lumps of maple sugar and sucked the cubes for sore throats. The Ojibwa also used the root juice for sore throats.

Iroquois women, as the Delaware, found bloodroot useful in several ways for some of their particular problems. Iroquois of both sexes used the plant for a variety of purposes associated with blood: as a dressing for cuts and wounds, for hemorrhages or ulcers, boils and sores. In these cases, we are probably seeing a case of the widespread notion that in medieval Europe was called the "doctrine of signatures," indicated the uses to which they were to be put. The red juice of the rhizome of the bloodroot is, no doubt, the color of blood. By the same logic, one uses the lobed leaf of the "liverleaf", *Hepatica spp.*, for liver ailments, and goldenrod or dandelion for jaundice.

Be that as it may, there is no denying that bloodroot, a member of the poppy family and closely related to the opium poppy, contains several physiologically active principles. It was long used in American medicine as a tonic and expectorant, and in larger doses as an emetic. It was also used externally for eczema and skin cancers. In only moderate doses, bloodroot is a potentially lethal poison, and *there are no legitimate reasons to use it internally today.*

There is one *excellent* contemporary use for bloodroot. It grows in thick lush carpets in eastern and northern woods, and it is among the very earliest of our spring wild flowers. Sending up a short tube, the leaf unfurls, disclosing the vibrant white eight-petaled flower. The brilliant flower has a very curious quality: sustained experimentation suggests that it cannot be photographed! Here is a glorious early spring day—after a long cold winter, one is eager to get out of doors and take the first flower pictures of the year. And there are vast beds of bloodroot—rich green lobed leaves, vivid white flowers, some of them with the vaguest hint of pink. Lying on my belly on the cold damp ground, I take a dozen shots—top, side, yes, even from the bottom up. A few days later, I examine my prints or slides. There is the deep green of the leaves, the rich moist brown leaf mold soil. The flower? It is inevitably overexposed, a white eight-petaled blank, rather as if I had photographed the electronic flash. Those vibrant flowers must contain a fluorescent compound of some kind that just doesn't interact very well with the film in the yellow box. So where am I? I cannot capture the flower's glow in material form. And those charming blooms last only a few weeks. I have to capture their spring radiance in my memory. That memory cheers me now—as I look out at the blanket of snow atop the wren house, and see a junco, one of our winter companions, flitting about the sunflower feeder. For I know that in 10 or 12 weeks the snow will be melted away and the bloodroot will be pushing up through the dank leaf mold, and I will try again—a filter perhaps, or another kind of film—lying on my belly on the cool ground of spring.

The Indians of Virginia, according to John Smith writing in 1612, adorned themselves with the color of the bloodroot to enhance their virile charms. Helped them get the blood running maybe. Perhaps I'll do the same and sacrifice one of the little flowers, and rub the red juice on my hands and cheeks. But I will probably just look at them, and lie on the ground (fruitlessly) clicking my camera, and store away an unphotographable memory, for another winter day.

## Blue flag, the rainbow flower.

### Iris versicolor

It is certainly true that many medicinal plants are beautiful ones, but perhaps the blue flags, various species of the genus *Iris*, are the most beautiful. Among the two dozen North American iris species, two in particular were widely used as medicines by native Americans, the wild iris, *I. missouriensis*, and the blue flag, *I. versicolor*.

The predominant use of the flags was as poultices for various aches, pains, and wounds. The Chippewa, Montagnais, and Mohegan used a mashed root poultice for swollen rheumatic joints while the Fox and Omaha used the same thing on burns, sores or bruises. The Potawatomi used the mashed root to reduce inflammation on cuts and sores. The Cherokee boiled the root with fat to make a salve for sores. Wild iris was a favored remedy of the Paiute and Shoshone who held the raw root against aching teeth to reduce toothache pain; they also collected the seeds and ground them to a paste which they applied to sores, and, along with the Omaha, they used the boiled root tea topically to soothe earaches.

The plants were also used internally for a number of purposes. The Delaware ate the roots for rheumatism, and the Fox ate them as a general cold remedy. The Paiute and Shoshone drank the boiled root tea for stomach aches. Several groups used the plant as an emetic or cathartic, among them the Navajo, Iroquois, and Ojibwa. The Aleuts used the boiled root tea of beachhead iris, *I. hookeri*, as a laxative.

The Penobscot considered blue flag to be a particularly powerful medicine and used the boiled root tea as a cure for cholera. The Delaware mixed the root with a species of hydrangia and drank it to break up gallstones.

Several species of iris are used medicinally in China in similar ways. One species, *Iris tectorum*, was considered particularly useful in dispelling evil influences, and it was used for a number of wasting diseases.

The genus has a checkered European history. It was apparently

*BLUE FLAG:* Iris versicolor. *The showy flower of this blue-violet iris has darkly veined sepals. Yellow marks accent the bases of the petals. The plant has pale green, grass-like leaves which rise two to three feet from a thick, creeping rootstock. Found in ditches, marshes and meadows, Blue flag blooms all summer.*

Clovis I, King of the Francs in the sixth century, who adopted the yellow water-flag, *Iris pseudoacorus*, as his emblem (an anthropologist probably prefers to think of it as a totem). Only later in the 12th century did Louis VII adopt the flower for his symbol during the crusades; subsequently it became known as the "fleur de Louis," the source of the current term, fleur de lis. The various flag species were widely used medicinally in Europe in much the same ways as was sweet flag, *Acorus calamus*, with which the root was sometimes confused. It was considered good for sores and cuts, and for stomach disturbances. It was also deemed effective for bruises or black eyes which would quickly clear up when bandaged with a plaster made of the root.

The dried roots of blue flag were official in the USP from 1820 until 1895, and were recommended for use on wounds and sores and as one of the inevitable purges, cathartics and diuretics of 19th century medicine.

This is one of those plants which today belongs not in the medicine cabinet but in the garden. The most magnificent fields of blue flag I have ever seen were in some of the high meadows of the Black Hills in South Dakota—thousands of blooms stretching off as far as I could see. Seek them out with your camera. You will be in ancient company. Thutmose III, Pharoah of Egypt in the 15th century BC, brought back Iris with him after he conquered Syria, and included it in his stone "botanical garden" at his temple at Karnak in Thebes. A small room in the temple has several hundred flowers carved on the walls, representing the Pharoah's efforts in natural history. In the 3500 years since, gardeners have been tinkering with the flags so that now you can get them in any color of the rainbow ('Iris' is Greek for rainbow). But none are more lovely than the nodding wild ones, reflecting back the sky in their glory.

*BURDOCK:* Arctium minus. *The two to five-foot burdock plants have broad, oval leaves and lavender flower heads covered by long bur-forming bristles. Burdock found in waste lands and along fence rows, blooms from July to October.*

## Burdock, lover of humanity.

### *Arctium minus*

Burdock is easy to find. Indeed it is sometimes too easy to find; it finds you. The prickly round burs catch on clothing, shoes, and especially on wool shirts; usually the only way to get them off is to crumble the burs and pick out the little pieces one at a time. And, in the process, you are acting as an agent of dispersal for the plant, spreading its seeds. It is perhaps not surprising that this Eurasian plant was rapidly introduced to the new world, and quickly dispersed across North America. Pliny reports that the Greeks sarcastically called the burdock *philanthropos,* or "lover of man," because of its habit of sticking to clothes. He went on to say that a small wreath of the leaves worn on the head relieved headaches.

The plant was adopted as a medicine by numerous native American groups. Several eastern tribes used the roots or leaves in boiled teas or as poultices for boils, abscesses, or sores. The Mohegan applied a poultice of leaves to rheumatic joints while the Delaware drank a boiled root tea for the same problem. The Ojibwa used the root in a medicine for stomach pain. The Chippewa used a tea of the leaves and the Omaha used a boiled tea of the root as cough medicines. The Delaware, Potawatomi, and Cherokee all considered the plant to be a useful blood purifier, and the Ojibwa used it as a tonic.

For the Iroquois, burdock was considered one of the most powerful of plants. This followed from several of its characteristics, all of which indicated its dangers. First, it has burs, *prima facie* evidence to the Iroquois of power. Second, it was used to cure vague internal pains, cysts, boils, and piles, all understood by the Iroquois to be consequences of witchcraft; the plant was powerful enough to be used to counteract witchcraft. Third, witches were known to use the plant to cause bad luck, accidents, and death. The burdock root was carved into the shape of the intended victim, and the witch stabbed it with a pointed stick. Fortunately, a boiled root tea of burdock was often strong enough to counteract this witchcraft. Interestingly enough, the Iroquois seem to have agreed with the Greeks: burdock leaves tied on the head were considered a cure for headaches.

The root of *Arctium lappa* was in the USP from 1831 to 1842, and again from 1851 to 1916. It was considered a mild purgative and diuretic, and was also used on cuts, sores, and other skin ailments. While the Menominee used this species, all the other native American groups considered here used another closely related species, *Arctium minus*.

The only legitimate medicinal uses of burdock have shrunk lately. Aspirin is certainly a more convenient (if less colorful) remedy for headache than wearing a garland of burdock leaves; and on a sore or boil, I would have more confidence in an antibiotic ointment than in burdock root. But the plant can yet serve us well. Like the old chestnut about the Boy Scout who did his good deed by escorting across the street the old woman who didn't want to go, burdock, "philanthropos," is one of those things in the world which urges us to caution as we attempt to help our fellow humans. It is hard to know sometimes what is best for oneself; it is only harder to know what is good for someone else. A measure of a true lover of mankind is that his acts of compassion are truly directed to others rather than to himself. Of this the burdock can remind us every time we walk through the woods.

## Catnip, feline marijuana.

### *Nepeta cataria*

Catnip is an introduced European species, a member of the mint family, with an ancient history there as a tonic and sedative. It was adopted medicinally by a half dozen northeastern tribes who used it in a similar fashion. The Ojibwa used a boiled leaf tea as a blood purifier or as a general tonic. The Menominee and Chippewa used the boiled tea to break fevers. The Menominee used this treatment for pneumonia; the patient drank the liquid and was bathed with it.

Catnip was often found to be a particularly good medicine for children. The Mohegan used leaf tea to treat colic in infants. The Cherokee, Delaware and Menominee used boiled leaf tea to soothe fretful babies and to help them sleep. The Delaware also compounded catnip leaves with peach seeds to make a syrup which was considered to be a very valuable tonic for children. The Iroquois used leaf tea for restless, peevish or feverish babies. They also gave the tea to children with upset stomachs or diarrhea; they strengthened this tea with bloodroot for adult use.

Catnip has been a popular household remedy in Europe for centuries, though it has not been an official part of professional medicine. In 1633, Gerard noted that catnip was used in baths for women to sit over, "to bring down their sickness, and to make them fruitful." In China, a related species known as ground ivy, *Nepeta glechoma*, has long been used for fevers and pains, especially toothaches and earaches.

The most curious thing about catnip, of course, is its effect on cats. The substance in the plant which so excites cats is called nepetalacetone. The chemical has certain structural similarities to the "indole ring" which shows up in many hallucinogens like psilocybin, serotonin and harmaline. There is little evidence that catnip is an effective human hallucinogen, but, smoked like marijuana, it may have some mild mind-altering capabilities. The most one should expect from catnip, however, is a mild sedative effect, similar to that of hops or camomile. A tea made of equal parts of

*CATNIP:* Nepeta cataria. *The white or pale purple flowers arranged on spikes at the ends of branched, two to three-foot stems, bloom from June to September. Arrowhead shaped, jaggedly toothed leaves with white undersides are arranged oppositely on the square stem. Found in wet places.*

catnip and mint is a pleasant after dinner drink, heathful if for no reason other than the fact that catnip is a rich source of vitamin C. Catnip is very easily grown in an herb garden or in flower beds. The only difficulty is that once the neighborhood cats find the patch, they are liable to destroy it posthaste. It is humorous enough to watch that the loss of the plants is small price to pay.

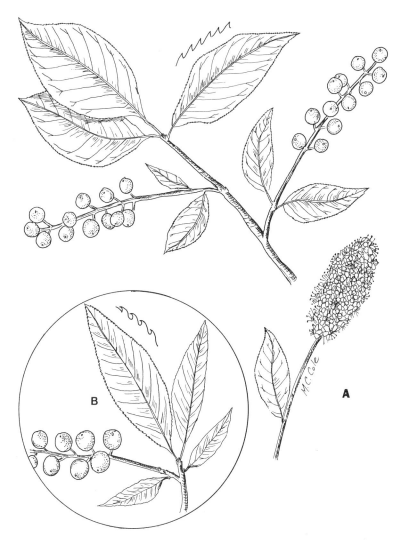

(**A**) *CHOKECHERRY:* Prunus virginiana. *Without careful examination, these cherries are easily confused. The chokecherry has wide oval leaves, two to four inches long, with sharply pointed teeth. Clusters of white flowers produce dark red cherries, about one-third inch in diameter.*

(**B**) *BLACK CHERRY:* Prunus serotina. *Wild black cherry differs by having larger, narrower, more finely toothed leaves. The black fruits are about half an inch in diameter. At maturity, both trees have scaly black bark.*

## Cherries, Plums and Peaches; The sweet genus Prunus.

*Prunus virginiana*

*Prunus serotina*

*Prunus americana*

*Prunus Persica*

In our chapter on elderberries, we considered the conceptual differences between medicine and food, and suggested that the difference was essentially one of context, or intention. However, it is more complicated than that. If we look at the plant kingdom as a whole, and at human use of plants as a whole, it turns out that, by and large, foods and drugs are discontinuous categories.

There are approximately 17,000 species of plants in North America. About 1500 species, or nine percent, have been used medicinally by native Americans. Botanists have classified these species into some 231 families. By and large, families which are the source of important food plants are not important sources of medicinal plants, and vice versa. Generally speaking, the most important family for human foods is the Poaceae, or grass family. All of our important cultivated grains—wheat, barley, corn, rice, millet—come from this family. There are in North America nearly 1500 species of grasses yet only some 17 of them (about one percent) were used medicinally. By contrast, the vast Asteraceae, or sunflower, family is only a modest source of human foods—sunflower seeds were a minor food for some peoples, and some species provide edible greens (probably the most important species for us is lettuce). But about nine percent of the Asteraceae species were used medicinally. And the pine family (Pinaceae), another family which produces only a few foods (like pine nuts), has about 70 North American species of which about half were used medicinally. Generally, then, families which produce foods don't produce drugs, and families which produce drugs don't produce foods. There are a few exceptions to this rule, and they are very interesting. Consider the rose family, Rosaceae. Nearly half of

(A) *WILD PLUM*: Prunus americana. *Wild plum is a small tree or shrub with smooth, oblong leaves with closely-set marginal teeth. Two to four of the one-inch white flowers grow in clusters. Fruits are reddish and round. The inner flesh is yellow; the fruit stone is flat.*
(B) *PEACH*: Prunus Persica. *The flowers of the peach are large and pink. The familiar fruit has a sculptured stone. Having escaped cultivation, the wild peach grows in thickets, and along roadsides.*

the 53 North American genera in this family were used medicinally by native Americans. This, by our generalization, should lead us to predict that the rose family would not be an important source of foods. But it is, and what wonderful foods, at that! Apples, peaches, plums, prunes, apricots, cherries, nectarines, quinces, strawberries, raspberries, blackberries, loganberries, and almonds, among others, are all members of this extraordinary family. Where would we be without them? Not only is the *family* the source of both foods and drugs, but one genus in the family could, by itself, stock both a substantial drug store *and* a fruit stand.

The genus *Prunus* includes the cherries, plums and peaches. There is, of course, no need to discuss the use of these as foods. But these species also have many medicinal uses. At least four species of cherries were used medicinally by native Americans. The choke-cherry, *Prunus virginiana*, and the wild black cherry, *P. serotina*, were often used interchangably as cough medicines, antidiarrheals, cold remedies, and so on. The Mohegan and Ojibwa, for example, used a boiled black cherry bark tea to make a cold remedy while the Paiute used choke-cherry bark for this purpose. The Delaware made a stimulating tonic from black cherry bark, while the Thompson Indians and Potawatomi used choke-cherry bark this way.

Cherries were also used externally on wounds and sores by several tribes. The Ojibwa, for example, added the inner bark of black cherry to a salve for sores. The Menominee pounded the inner bark of the choke-cherry for use as a poultice on wounds, and the Paiute pulverized the dried choke-cherry bark and sprinkled it on sores to dry them up.

Cherry bark has long been a part of Western medicine, largely as a cough or cold remedy. The bark of either choke or black cherry was listed in the USP from 1820 until 1970. For the first hundred years or so it was recommended as a tonic and stimulant as well as a cough remedy. For the latter fifty years, and still today, it was used generally as a flavoring agent, especially for very salty or bitter drugs.

The plums were also used medicinally. The wild plum, *Prunus americana*, was a favorite remedy of the Chippewa who used the root bark for intestinal parasites; they also used the bark as a disinfectant for wounds as did the Omaha. The Fox used the root bark as an astringent poultice for canker sores on the mouth. The plums were never official in western medicine, but were occasionally used in folk practice. The Paiute used the desert peach, *Prunus andersonii*, in a number of ways, as an antidiarrheal, cold remedy, and for the pain of rheumatism. For these purposes, they used the leaves of the cultivated peach, *Prunus Persica*, for fevers and high blood pressure.

Persic oil, derived from peach pits, was listed in the USP from 1942 until 1960. It was used largely as an emollient in salves, and was a substitute for a similar oil derived from almonds which were unavailable during the Second World War.

Now, here comes the clincher. The cherries, peaches and plums, sources of a variety of excellent foods which we all eat regularly, and which have supplied medicines for many peoples for centuries, are potentially lethal poisons, and the internal medicinal uses mentioned here *should not be tried by anyone*. The reason for this is that the bark, leaves and pits of most of the *Prunus* species, and several other members of the rose family including apples and pears, contain a substance called amygdalin. When mixed with water, amygdalin decomposes and produces prussic or hydrocyanic acid, a potentially lethal poison very similar to cyanide. People have been killed by eating apple pits; livestock have suffered serious and occasionally fatal poisoning from eating choke-cherry leaves; eight or nine bitter almond nuts are fatal for children, and three can cause severe cyanide poisoning.

The key to this problem, as is often the case with medicines, is the relationship between a medicinal dose and a lethal one. Many medicines, of course, are therapeutic in a small dose and poisonous in a larger one. The measure of safety in a drug is the *difference* between these two doses. And since individual tolerances vary, in this case where that difference is rather small, it is probably best not to take any chances.

Fortunately, the *fruits* of the *Prunus* species do not contain amygdalin! And, everyone knows that "an apple a day keeps the doctor away." Perhaps the same is true of cherries, plums and peaches. It is certainly worth trying. This is the kind of exception to a scientific principle that is really worth while.

## Columbine, the Love Flower

### *Aquilegia canadensis*

It is appropriate, I suppose, that as charming a flower as the columbine must be discussed with a certain delicacy. The plant, related to the aconite, or monkshood, is potentially poisonous, and should not be taken internally in any way. Some native American groups did so use it; in most cases, they (the Fox, Ojibwa, and Shoshone) used it for gastrointestinal problems, probably for intestinal parasites, that is, as a vermifuge. Vermifuges, being poisons, are always dangerous, and they are unlikely to be needed by any readers of this book. Some Western tribes ground the seeds and vigorously rubbed them into the hair to kill head lice, again evidence of the poisonous qualities of the plant, and again for a problem rare these days.

But there are other much more reasonable and delightful uses for the plant, though they too have their dangers but of a different sort. Before I describe these uses, I must make a seemingly old-fashioned request and urge that ladies read no further—the ethnographic record suggests that this use was for men only, and balancing discretion against complete reporting demands that I make this request.

Now, gentlemen, I note that the men of at least three native American groups used the seeds of the columbine as a love charm, an infallible technique for turning the heads of their intended ladies. I must now balance my request that ladies remain ignorant of this use by urging all of you to use the utmost judgement and good taste if you are persuaded to attempt this extremity— remembering that the measure of a man is the restraint with which he employs his advantage.

So, among the Omaha Indians, a young man would rub the pulverized seeds of the columbine on the palms of his hands; then, he would contrive to shake hands with his intended lover. This was deemed a certain love charm which would surely turn the head of his intended. A more subtle technique used by both the Omaha and Ponca involved crushing the seeds with a bit of water to form a

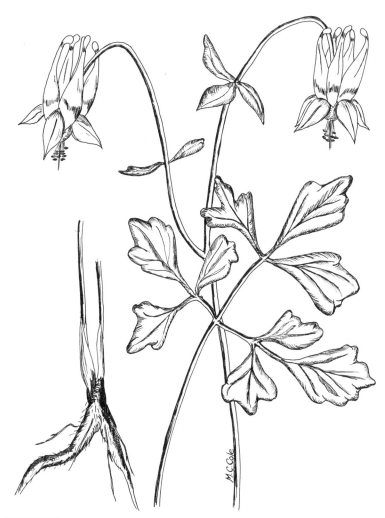

COLUMBINE: Aquilegia canadensis. *The beautiful red flowers of the Columbine each have five long curved spikes or nectaries. The leaves of this one to two-foot tall plant are divided, then subdivided in threes. Columbines bloom in rocky woods and on slopes from April to July.*

paste which was dabbed on clothing. The seeds thus provided a lasting fragrance enhanced whenever moistened by rain or dew. Young Fox Indians also employed columbine seeds as an alluring perfume, adding another twist by mixing the seeds into their smoking tobacco to make it smell elegant, refined.

One measure of the reputation of this plant among midwestern tribes is that mischievious Omaha boys would harass girls by suddenly thrusting some of the powder under their noses. Since too strong a smell of the seeds might cause a nosebleed, this ruffianism would inevitably cause a tumultuous retreat by the victims. The distinction between youthful high jinks and drug abuse is sometimes a narrow one.

There are, I noted earlier, certain dangers involved in this aspect of columbine, though we find them in European rather than native American tradition. Examine the elegant form of the columbine bloom and you will see five graceful spikes at the rear of the bloom. Our name for the plant comes from the Latin *columbinus*, resembling the dove; some saw the five nectaries as resembling a group of doves or pigeons. But look again, and see if they don't also resemble the cuckold's horns.

In the fourth act of Shakespeare's *Hamlet*, Ophelia, by now mad, has attained a true clarity of vision escaping all the others. She rambles on, dispersing flowers to the principals: to Hamlet, rosemary for remembrance, and pansies for thoughts; to the Queen, rue for sorrow, and daisies for the light of love; and to Claudius, fennel for flattery, and columbine for cuckoldry. Laertes notes, "This nothing's more than matter."

George Chapman, a contemporary of Shakespeare, in his play *Al fooles, a comedy*, has a character say, for the same reasons, "What' that? A columbine? No: that thankless flower grows not in *my* garden."

There are, then, dangers in charms as in any other medicines, even if only metaphorical ones. But certainly these dangers do not warrant excluding the columbine from the garden. For this is its true role in a modern herbal—to grace shady places with its subtle nodding blooms, its soft translucent leaves. The plant has inspired generations of gardeners who have produced a profusion of showy strains—blue, white, red, coral—some of them with immense flowers two or three inches long. None are more beautiful, more charming, than the wild natural forms. The seeds or rooted plants are readily purchased at your garden supply store. They thrive in acid soil (dig in some peat moss) in shady spots. These perennial plants will last for several years before they lose their vigor; then try digging them up, dividing the roots, and replanting with new peat and perhaps some acid fertilizer.

The presence of this graceful plant may alone add sufficient charm to your bearing that you need not go to the extremity of grinding the seeds and spreading them about the house.

## The Purple Coneflower of the Great Plains

### *Echinacea angustifolia*

The purple coneflower, *Echinacea angustifolia*, a favored medicine among many tribes throughout its range in the American and Canadian plains, is one of the finest medicinal plants for the contemporary flower garden. Extremely hardy perennial varieties can be grown from seed; the three foot tall plants produce startling purple-red blossoms up to 4 or 5 inches across, occasionally larger in some horticultural varieties.

The plant was widely used by native American groups in the plains—the Dakota, Omaha, Pawnee, Winnebago, Fox, Cheyenne, and Comanche—for several purposes. Several of these groups used it for snakebites, although it is not clear exactly what part of the plant was used, or how. It was also used for insect bites and stings. The plant was burned and the smoke inhaled for headaches; a similar treatment was considered effective for distemper in horses. It was widely used as a topical remedy for toothache.

The most common use of the plant was as a treatment for burns which were bathed with the juice of the plant. The plant was also put in steam baths to make the intense heat more bearable. It was apparently also used by magicians who squeezed the juice on their arms to render them insensitive to heat—they could then, it was said, plunge their hands into boiling water without pain, to the amusement of the audience! One Winnebago informant told the great ethnobotanist Melvin Gilmore that he used the plant to make his *mouth* insensitive to heat—he could then place live coals in his mouth! He did not, apparently, demonstrate this trick for the anthropologist.

The Sioux used the root for colic or bowel pain, and the Fox used the root in a compound for stomach aches and convulsions. The Comanche used the root to treat sore throats.

The plant had some reputation among whites as a cure for venereal diseases; it was also used topically to treat skin rashes and eczema. The root was official in the NF from 1916 until 1950, and

*(A) NARROW-LEAVED PURPLE CONEFLOWER:* Echinacea angustifolia. **(B)** *PURPLE CONE-FLOWER:* Echinacea purpurea. *The single purple-rayed flowers of the Narrow Leaved Cone-flower are arranged on slender hair stems. The lance-shaped, hairy leaves have three prominent veins. The plants grow one to two feet tall in dry soils. In contrast, the Purple Coneflower differs by having oval toothed leaves and smooth stems. It also varies in habitat, growing in moist rich soils.*

was considered a useful stimulating tonic or "alterative."

The biggest problem with the medicinal use of purple coneflower is that, to use it, you have to dig up the plant which, otherwise, would continue to grace your garden with its glorious flowers. It is a particularly decisive case of a zero-sum game: you can't have your flowers and eat them too.

## Culver's root

### *Veronicastrum virginicum*

To recite the native American and 18th and 19th century Euro-American uses of the root of this charming member of the snap-dragon family is to become somewhat bilious.

The Menominee, Chippewa, Southern Ojibwa, and Fox all used the root of the plant as either a laxative or a cathartic. Steeping the root in hot water gave the laxative; boiling it for a while gave the much stronger and more violent cathartic purge which also produced intense vomiting. The Menominee and Chippewa considered this medicine as a purifier of sorts—the former used it in any case of defilement, the latter in cases of "scrofula," that is, tuberculosis of the lymph glands.

Among the American colonists, the drug became a quite common, if not "popular," purge. At one time or another it was used for pleurisy and other chest afflictions, as well as for syphillis. The drug was listed under several different names in the USP from 1820 to 1840 and again from 1864 until 1916, and in the NF from 1916 until 1955. Improving on the simpler techniques of the Indians, western physicians developed several more efficient ways of concentrating the purgative principle, typically involving alcohol extraction. This effective technique produced an even more violent purge than the older methods.

The whole thing seems rather bizarre. In our current view, violent vomiting and diarrhea seem to us the *symptoms* of illness, things to be *stopped*, rather than the cure for illness. The only time that emesis (vomiting) is considered to be appropriate therapy is if someone has swallowed poison for which we are told we should keep handy a bottle of Ipecac, a strong emetic derived from the roots of a South American plant *Cephaelis ipecacuanha*.

These different points of view indicate a fundamental change that has occurred in our view of the world in the past century. Until very recently, disease was understood to be not the result of the interaction of a person and a virus or bacteria, but rather a consequence of a disruption of the person's "balance." In classic

European tradition, this balance was understood to follow from the interaction of the person's four "humors." The residue of this system of thought is still very much alive in English speech. The four humors were blood, black bile, yellow bile, and phlegm. The blood was known as "sanguine"—a person with an excess of blood would be cheerful, optimistic, unconcerned, "sanguine." One with an excess of "black bile," that is, blood from the spleen, would be "melancholic," literally meaning "black bile." Some contemporary schools of psychiatry still tell us (as does much folk wisdom) that to cure depression, you should "let it all hang out," or, in a more ancient idiom, "vent your spleen." An excess of "choler," yellow bile from the gall bladder, would make you jaundiced—skeptical, irritable, angry, suspicious, "choleric." Finally, an excess of phlegm made one stolid, imperturbable, unshakeable, in a word, "phlegmatic." Summing up, this state of balance determined whether or not a person was in a good "humor."

Humors in the Hippocratic tradition each has a "temperature" which was a combination of two dichotomies: hot-cold, and wet-dry. Blood was hot and wet, yellow bile was hot and dry, phlegm was cold and wet, while black bile was cold and dry. Today, we speak of one person's "hot temper(ature)," of another's "cold" personality, of another's "dry humor"; an ultimate insult is to suggest that someone is "all wet."

The essential quality of this theory was that illness was a function purely of the person himself, of his own constitution. The solution to illness then was to restructure the patient's humoral balance. One did this by removing the offending, excessive humor by the purge (either "from above or below") or by bleeding. This idea, expressed in varying degrees, was the primary theory in medicine for two thousand years in the West. Also, with variations (usually omitting the bleeding), it was the theory in many native American societies.

Perhaps the most extreme form of this medical theory was announced in about 1800 by a famous American physician. Benjamin Rush can easily be listed among the "Founding Fathers." A signer of the Declaration of Independence and a leading citizen of Philadelphia, the cultural and intellectual center of 18th century America, Rush is best known today as the "Father of Psychiatry"

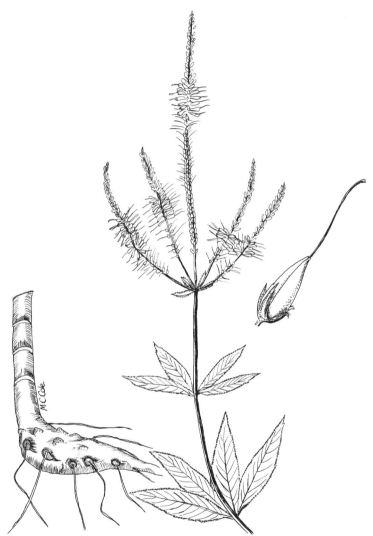

*CULVER'S ROOT:* Veronicastrum virginicum. *The smooth, sharp-toothed, slender leaves of Culver's root are arranged in whorls of three to nine around the stem. Tubular purplish or white flowers are borne on a flower stalk. The fruit is an oblong capsule, one to fifteen inches long. The plant blooms from June to September in moist meadows, thickets and rich woods.*

due to his famous book "Medical Inquiries and Observations upon Diseases of the Mind" which was, in 1812, revolutionary in that it argued convincingly that mental illness had physical causes, was not the work of demons, and was amenable to medical treatment. It was a most humanitarian work. He is less famous today for the work which was more influential at the time, and, I fear, a good deal less humanitarian. Rush argued that there was really only one disease (not four, or four hundred) which expressed itself in a multitude of ways.

The disease was a "fever" brought on by an "excessive action" of the blood vessels, a kind of hypertension. To cure sickness (any sickness), one should "reduce the tension" by bleeding and purging. Although there was only one disease, it came in varying intensities, and, it seemed to follow, the more serious the disease, the more "heroic" treatment should be. The great historian of American medicine, Richard Shryock, has noted the curious experimental verification of this argument: "Anyone could see that, if the patient were bled copiously enough, he would relax—sooner or later!" During the first half of the 19th Century, American language changed—when ill, one would no longer report that he was recovering from his sickness, but (if all went as well as possible) that he was surviving the treatments. To this day, the journal of the British Medical Society is named after one of the infamous instruments of this theory: it is the *Lancet.* The other most favored treatment was not a botanical product but mercurous chloride, known to all as Calomel. But it was supplemented by dozens of other drugs, most of them botanical, many of them represented in these pages, which in one way or another caused the patient to purge himself, to eliminate offensive humors, in one conceptualization or another.

This chapter is not meant to suggest that our predecessors were completely wrong. That a person's constitution may not *be* a disease is certainly true. But, if in reaction to the excesses of the 19th century we fail to recognize that one's constitution *influences* disease, we throw out the baby with the bath. "Stress," the body's reaction to fear or danger, is known to cause serious illness; recent research has shown that in certain kinds of laboratory rats which are highly susceptible to cancer, stressed rats had more cancer than non-stressed ones. And stress can reduce the efficiency with which the immunological system works, making people more likely to "catch" diseases to which they are exposed.

Culver's Root is a tall graceful plant, found in damp wooded areas, along streams and banks. By far the best use for its noxious root is to be left in the ground, to nourish the creamy white flowers and to remind us of a reasonable and ancient idea run amok.

## Dandelions, the Lion's teeth

### *Taraxacum officinale*

Rarely has a plant had such swings in popularity as has the homely dandelion. The subject of glorious praise for its medicinal virtue for the several centuries preceding ours, it is now the prime target of large industrial combines producing selective herbicides; our current attitudes seem to resemble those of the Greek naturalist Theophrastus who, in the fourth century BC, marvelled at its ability to flower over and over again each season, but otherwise dismissed it as being "unfit for food, and bitter." Down, up, down; A Nixonian sort of reputation.

While the common dandelion of North America was introduced from Europe, there are some 16 native species, although most of them are confined to Alaska or Greenland. Native Americans used the plant as a food—as an early season edible herb—and also as a medicine. Both the Bella Coola of British Columbia and the Ojibwa of the Midwest used a tea of the root for stomach pain or heartburn; the Fox used the same preparation for chest pain. The Papago used a tea of the blossoms for menstrual cramps while the Navajo used a strong root tea to hasten the delivery of the placenta after childbirth. The Tewa of the Southwest used the ground leaves as a dressing to speed the healing of broken bones.

The plant was listed in the U.S. Pharmacopeia as an official drug from 1831 to 1926, and in the National Formulary from 1926 until 1965; it was recommended as a diuretic, tonic, and mild cathartic, or laxative. It was also considered to be highly beneficial for liver ailments of any sort. Several native American groups used it for similar purposes. The Delaware used a tea of the root and leaves as a laxative and tonic; the Mohegan used a strong tea of dried leaves as a cathartic. The Mohegan and Potawatomi used the root tea as a tonic. The Iroquois used dandelions along with wild clover and rhubarb in a tea for "liverspots"; they also used it for jaundice because, of course, the flower is yellow. They also used the leaf tea as a diuretic for "dropsy."

The Iroquois had another use for the plant, less in keeping with

*DANDELION:* Taraxacum officinale. *The familiar dandelion, with its yellow, many-flowered head, deeply-cut leaves, and long tap root, is a common plant of gardens, lawns, fields and roadsides.*

the western tradition, and one often found for plants with long tap roots. When a plant is found with an appropriately forked root, especially one with a smaller root in the fork hence resembling male anatomy, the name of one's intended lover was spoken several times. Then the finder threw the root behind him or herself—the lover would surely follow. As a variation on this procedure, dandelion roots found growing twined together were boiled hard in a quart of water, and face and fingers were washed in the cooled liquid. This procedure was repeated if it was not immediately successful in making the user sexually irresistible.

Our common name for the plant is apparently derived from the Latin term of medieval scholars, 'dens leonis,' lions teeth, which these early botanists fancied as a technical description of the leaves. In French, this became "dent de leon," and subsequently in English, dandelion. The current technical name is, curiously, a Latinized version of an Arabic corruption of a Persian original. The Persian term *talkh chakok* mimics Theophrastus as it means "bitter herb." The Arabic version *tarakhshagog* is the source of our Latinized *Taraxacum.*

The great virtue of dandelions, of course, is their availability. Being certain that no one has beaten you to your source and applied any herbicides, collect the leaves early in the spring for a pleasant and nutritious salad or pot herb (used like spinach). A tea of the dried leaves may be used in the evening as a mild sedative, and the roasted ground roots make a stimulating substitute for coffee, or an interesting addition to your favorite blend, in the manner of chicory. I am unsure of the effect of coffee made of appropriately forked or twisted roots, but experiments may be in order. If they prove successful, this humble but tenacious herb may well be in for a new surge of popularity.

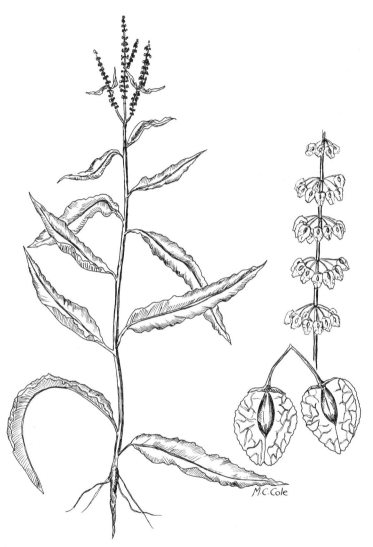

*YELLOW DOCK:* Rumex crispus. *Spikes of many small, whorled, scale-like flowers rise above the large wavy leaves. The stalked fruits become reddish-brown in late summer. This common, one to four-foot tall plant has a long tap root. It grows in fields and waste places.*

## Dock, the sword swallower's friend.

### *Rumex crispus*

Yellow dock is one of the great European immigrants to North America. It is found from Florida to Alaska and from Texas to Hudson's Bay, growing in neglected fields, waste places, along roadsides—it is the English sparrow of the world of weeds. Long used in European medical practice—both Pliny (in the 1st century) and Gerard (in the 17th) recommended ground dock root as a salve for sores—the plant was rapidly taken up by native Americans and used along side a half dozen native species of the genus.

Following the experience of their European predecessors, many tribes found dock useful for skin ailments. The Chippewa, Paiute, Shoshone and Ojibwa used the crushed root of yellow dock as a poultice for boils, sores, bruises, swellings or cuts. Other groups used the leaves, either fresh or dried and powdered, for the same purposes, while others used related species in the same fashion. For example, the Bella Coola used the mashed root of western dock, *Rumex occidentalis*, on cuts and boils.

The docks were a particularly favored remedy of some southwestern tribes, notably the Paiute. They used yellow dock as a blood purifier and for liver complaints, and sand dock, *Rumex venosus*, for rheumatism, as a cold remedy and cough medicine, and for stomach aches and kidney pains. They used either of these species as burn dressings, for bruises and sores, and as a general tonic.

Also from the southwest we find one of the more unusual uses of the docks, *Rumex mexicanus*, to soothe sore throats, particularly those caused by sword swallowing!

Several groups used one or another species of dock as a laxative or cathartic, notably the Shoshone.

The plant was widely recommended as a laxative or tonic in the past century. Its laxative action is probably due to the presence of a substance known as *emodin*, a peristaltic stimulant found in a number of plants including rhubarb roots and the cascara buckthorn as well as the docks. The wound healing qualities of the plant are probably a result of its rather substantial tannin content (see the discussion of tannin in our chapter on Sumac). One or another species of dock was listed in the USP from 1820 to 1905, recommended as a laxative and wound dressing. Our wandering yellow dock has also been used for these same purposes in China for at least 500 years.

Dock has often been considered little more than a pernicious and persistent weed. Shakespeare, in *Henry V*, has the Duke of Burgundy, while pleading for peace with the King, describe war torn France after the battle of Agincourt (1415) as a place where

> nothing teems
> But hateful docks, rough thistles, kecksies, burrs,
> Losing both beauty and utility.

A weed, of course, is a plant growing where you don't want it, a rose in the corn field, corn in the hedge. There may be weeds in your lawn, but weeds in a wilderness area are a contradiction in terms. Here, then, is a way to get rid of all the weeds. Declare your yard a wilderness area. Perhaps some of those colonizing docks will take up residence. You, then, could take up sword swallowing.

## Dogbane

### *Apocynum androsaemifolium*

Dogbane, *Apocynum androsaemifolium*, was a highly favored remedy of several northeastern tribes, notably the Chippewa, Ojibwa and Fox. The Chippewa and Ojibwa both used the root for headaches. The Chippewa would use several small bits of pulverized root as a snuff, or the powdered root was put on hot stones, whereupon the patient covered his head with a blanket and inhaled the fumes. The Ojibwa inhaled the smoke of the burning root for such headaches. The Chippewa fed a dilute boiled root tea to infants suffering from colds, and used a stronger boiled root tea topically for earaches. The Ojibwa used the same preparation to soothe sore throats.

The Fox used boiled root tea of the closely related Indian hemp, *Apocynum cannabinum*, for similar purposes, as a diuretic for "dropsy," for fever, and for a variety of other illnesses.

In all these uses, American 18th and 19th century medicine largely concurred. From 1831 until 1916, the Indian hemp was listed in the USP; dogbane was listed from 1820 until 1882. Both were recommended as cathartics, emetics and expectorants. However, more recent research has validated several additional native American uses of these species.

The Potawatomi used a boiled tea of the berries of dogbane as a heart medicine, while the Chippewa used a boiled root tea for "heart palpitations." Several species of the dogbane family have been shown to contain cardiotonic agents. In contemporary medicine, the best known cardiotonic plant is foxglove, *Digitalis purpurea*, a South American species. Many cardiotonic agents occur in the plant world; they act by slowing the heart's pace but strengthening its contractions. That these other agents do not find widespread use does not mean that they are not perfectly useful drugs; there is, however, no particular evidence that any of them are *better* than *Digitalis*, and so there has been no strong motivation to examine them closely.

These cardiotonic properties were, however, known to and exploited by some native Americans. Dogbane and Indian hemp

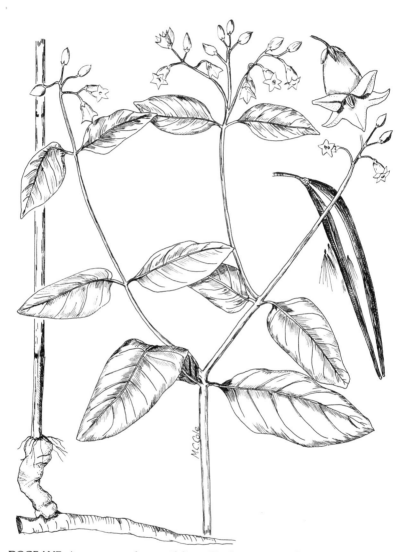

*DOGBANE:* Apocynum androsaemifolium. *Dogbane a two to four-foot tall plant, has smooth edged leaves arranged oppositely on a smooth, branched stem. The stem has tough, fibrous "bark" and milky juice. The small, bell-like flowers are white or pink. In the fall, long, dangling pods adorn these plants of fields and thickets.*

are potentially quite dangerous, and should be experimented with *very carefully*. While working in the Sea Islands in South Carolina, one elderly woman told me that Indian Hemp had been used, in the past, to induce abortions. These powerful plants may have this capacity, and so women should be *particularly* careful with them.

(A) *FLOWERING DOGWOOD:* Cornus florida. *The showy inflorescence of the flowering dog-wood is often mistaken for a single flower. It is a cluster of greenish-white flowers surrounded by four notched, petal-like bracts. The waxy green leaves have arching veins, and turn scarlet in the fall. The fifteen to forty-foot trees are found in rich woods.*
**(B)** *BUNCHBERRY:* Cornus canadensis. *The little bunchberry has a similar but much smaller flower head and a whorl of six leaves. The plant takes its name from the bright red berries which form in the fall. Found in cool, peaty woods.*

## Dogwood and bunchberry.

*Cornus florida*

*Cornus canadensis*

What might dogwood have to do with dogs? The answer is not clear. Some say that the term derives from an earlier name, Dog-berries, applied to the tree as a sort of slur indicating that the berries, unfit for human consumption, were fit only for dogs. An ancient source supporting this notion, that the berries of the dogwood are unfit for human consumption, comes from Homer. Odysseus, compelled to wander for 10 years before returning to Ithaca, lands at Aeaea, the Isle of Dawn, ruled by the Goddess Circe. She feasts many of his crew on fine (human) foods, like cheese, barley meal and honey with wine. But the food has been drugged. As the men pass out, Circe turns them into pigs, puts them in a sty, and feeds them again, this time with mean (animal) foods, like acorns, mast and the fruit of the cornel tree. But since this is not very complimentary to either the tree or to pigs or dogs, it may be worthwhile to look further. The wood of the dogwood is very hard, and long had a place in manufactures where it was used for making tools and handles for them, bearings, pulleys, and gears. An important item in many machines is known as a "dog," a term usually applied to a hook or claw-like element which controls the speed or direction of motion, often in association with a gear. Dogwood may have been named for its use in making these. Others, noting that English country butchers often used daggers (for killing hogs) made of the wood, suggest the sequence dagger-wood, dagwood, and then dogwood. Well, who can choose? Perhaps the tree was so called for three or four good reasons!

The genus *Cornus* (meaning "horn," as in cornucopia, and refer-ring, apparently, to the hardness of the wood) is a fascinating one comprising, in North America, a dozen species, most of them lovely and memorable. Perhaps the most charming is the bunch-berry or dwarf cornel, *Cornus canadensis*. This little plant with long runners is found in thick rich woods, its lovely white flowers in the early summer forming bright bunches of red berries later in the fall. The Delaware drank a boiled tea of the root bark for body aches and pains while the Ojibwa used boiled root tea to soothe colic in infants. The Carrier used a boiled tea of the whole plant as an eyewash, and the Thompson Indians burned the leaves and sprinkled the ash on wounds. The Iroquois used the boiled plant tea for coughs and fever. This species was never a significant part of western medicine and was never an official drug.

Silky cornel, *Cornus amomum*, is one of a number of plants that have been called "kinnikinik." The most common contemporary use of the term is as a name for bearberry, *Arctostaphylos uva-ursi*. But it *is* a Menominee word, and by the term they meant either the silky cornel or alternate-leaved cornel, *C. alternifolia*, which they collected for use as a smoking tobacco. The inner bark was shredded and toasted, and then smoked with much ceremony. They also used a bark tea of the silky cornel for treating diarrhea; when used this way its name was "maimakwukwa."

Other *Cornus* species were also used medicinally. The panicled dogwood, *C. racemosa*, was a favorite medicine of the Fox Indians who used a boiled bark tea as a toothache remedy and, in the form of an enema, as a remedy for diarrhea. They also burned the bark and used the smoke to revive someone who was unconscious.

Of course, the best known dogwood species is the flowering dogwood, *Cornus florida*. These graceful trees, with their pink-tinged white flowers always look to me as if they have stepped out of a Japanese screen painting. The Delaware used the root of the flowering dogwood in a compound taken as a tonic, and the Houma drank a boiled tea of scraped root bark for fevers. Several other eastern tribes used various formulations of flowering dogwood for fevers, and the practice was taken over by whites in various areas. Flowering dogwood was listed in the USP from 1820 until 1894 and was in the NF until 1936. Along with several official species, it was considered tonic and astringent, and was recommended as a wholly acceptable substitute for quinine for fevers.

The best known story about the flowering dogweed is the lovely Christian myth about the crucifixion of Jesus. The story goes that, in those days, the dogwood was a straight tall tree resembling the oak and was, therefore, a suitable wood for making the cross. Beacuse of its complicity in the murder of God, the tree felt great shame, but Jesus, holding it blameless, promised that, thereafter, it would grow low and crooked with blossoms in the form of the cross, showing at their margins the red and rusted marks of the nails, with the center cluster representing a golden crown of thorns. Since the flowering dogwood is a species native to North America which made no appearance in Europe or the Middle East until perhaps the 17th or 18th century, the tale cannot, in any historical sense, be true. My own feeling is that this doesn't matter very much; the story is such a good one that it carries with it another kind of truth, a kind of paradigmatic truth about redemption, or, if that word is a bit too strong, about renewal.

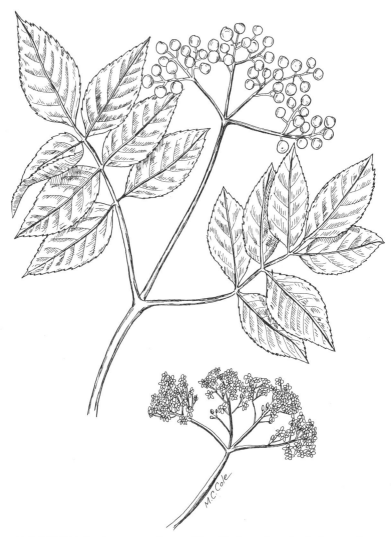

*ELDERBERRY:* Sambucus canadensis. *The elderberry is a shrub that reaches a height of six feet. The opposite leaves have five to eleven (usually seven) sharply toothed leaflets. Small, flat-topped clusters of white flowers mature to form the edible, purple-black fruits. The pith of the twig is white. Found in fields, moist woods, and along roadsides and railroad tracks.*

# Elderberry, food and medicine.

## *Sambucus canadensis*

"Take elderberries, clean them, and boil in water. Dry slightly and arrange in a greased shallow pan with a small stick. Add 6 scruples (about 1/4 ounce) of pepper, moisten with *liquamen*, then add one cyathus (about 3 tablespoons) each of *liquamen*, wine, and *passum*, mix well; finally put in the pan 4 oz. of oil, place in the hot ashes, and bring to the boil. When the mixture is boiling break 6 eggs over it, stir well, and so bind it. When it has set sprinkle with pepper and serve."[1]

This recipe, from a cookbook written by the Roman gastronome Apicius during the reign of Tiberius in the 1st century serves well to indicate the curious overlap in our categories of "food" and "medicine." For elderberry bushes have long been used both ways. Both the ancients and the native Americans used it as food and medicine, particularly as a purge and as a poultice for wounds and swellings (Dioscorides recommended it for mad dog bites).

What is the difference between "foods" and "drugs?" Usually we are clear enough about the distinction, and it isn't something that is likely to be confusing in ordinary life. Few are likely to confuse a hamburger with a shot of penicillin. But those items are at the "center" of the categories. What happens when we get closer to their edges? Consider orange juice. If you have a glass of orange juice with an English muffin for breakfast, the juice is food. If, however, you have scurvy and are told by a physician to drink 5 glasses of juice a day, then it seems reasonable to call the juice a drug. The problem here is that we are dealing with what we call a "vitamin." What is a vitamin? My dictionary says vitamins are "food factors essential in small quantities to maintain life but not themselves supplying energy." The problem with this definition is that it could as easily describe, say, insulin for a diabetic as it describes ascorbic acid for everyone, yet we certainly would

---

[1]. *Liquamen* is a sauce rather like Worcestershire made of fish and salt. *Passum* is a sweetened red wine. The recipe comes from a lovely translation of Apicius' book by Barbara Flower and Elisabeth Rosenbaum (London: Harrap Co. 1958).

consider insulin to be a drug, not a food or a vitamin. The difference, then, between drugs and vitamins on the one hand and food on the other would seem to be that the former are "essential to life." But this would suggest that food is not essential to life, which is just silly. So where are we?

It seems to me that the fundamental differences between food, vitamins, and drugs lie not in what these "things" are, but rather the contexts in which they are used. Suppose I am healthy as can be, but hungry. My wife, who has a terrible head cold, has no appetite at all. I go into the kitchen and make a beautiful pot of rich aromatic chicken soup. We sit down at the table, and, as I eat two bowls, I urge her to eat some because "it'll be good for you." Afterwards *I* feel better because I am no longer hungry. *She* feels better, because her head is less stuffed. (There *is* scientific evidence showing that chicken soup, "Jewish penicillin," has a distinct effect on stuffed sinus cavities, inducing significantly more "mucous movement" than a control substance, hot water.) The same pot of soup provided food for me and medicine for her, because of contextual differences—I was healthy, and she was ill.

Neither, however, is this the end of the problem, for the difference between being healthy or ill is not all that clear. I was as healthy as could be that day with the chicken soup. I felt vigorous and strong; indeed, I had spent the day before out in the yard turning over the garden and trimming trees, and, now that I think about it, my left shoulder hurts like blazes! (I've had trouble with that crummy shoulder for years.) Perhaps I ought to do something about it. A nice cup of hot milk before bed will relax me, and insure that I get a good night's sleep. My shoulder will be better in the morning.

Illness is a category which we apply to a smooth and continuous range of variation in our "comfort." (Note that illness is rather different from "injury.") We *decide* (often with the help of professional advice) whether or not we are ill. Some anthropologists differentiate between "disease" (destructive physiological process) and "illness" (conceptualization and definition of physiological state). Both my father and I have been told by physicians that we have arthritis in our hands. Both of us experience some discomfort, he more than I. More often than not, if we ignore it, it isn't very bothersome; while we both recognize the presence of disease, neither of us considers it an illness. There are individual differences in the way people conceptualize illness. Some people consider any little twinge to be some terrible disease; we number then among "hypochondriacs." Some people deny serious and painful symptoms, perhaps because they "really don't want to know." Both of these types are the bane of physicians.

Conceptualization of context is essential for differentiating illness from health, and food from drugs.

Native Americans used several species of elderberry medicinally in a variety of ways. Many tribes used a tea of the bark or root as a cathartic or emetic, among them the Carrier, Gitskan, Iroquois, Cherokee and Ojibwa. The Shoshone and Paiute used a tea of the blossoms as a cold and cough remedy, while the Menominee used the same formulation for reducing fevers. The Delaware and Paiute used various plant parts for poultices on scrapes, cuts and bruises. The Paiute ate the dried berries as an antidiarrheal, and the Houma fermented the berries to make a wine which they considered to be a tonic.

Various parts of the elderberry shrub, *Sambucus canadensis*, were official drugs for over a century, listed in the USP from 1820 until 1905, and in the NF from 1916 until 1947. It was used as a dressing for wounds and as an "alterative," that is, as a sort of tonic.

Generally, elderberries should not be eaten raw (they have a rank flavor anyway). The plant contains a number of alkaloids which are not well understood, and poses some dangers. Children using the hollow stems as peashooters have become quite ill as a result. Cooking the berries, however, renders them eminently edible, particularly in jams and jellies, and particularly when combined with acid fruits like crab apples or oranges. Packaged pectin (like Sure Jell or Certo) usually includes recipes for these jams which are well worth trying.

Elderberries are usually easy to find, and, in the fall, they are laden with great clumps of berries. One or two shrubs will often provide a bucketful of berries. I have found that the best place to find elderberries is along railroad tracks. I don't know why, but it always seems to work.

I haven't tried Apicius' recipe. I confess that elderberry omelet with salted fish sauce doesn't do a whole lot for me. But who knows, it may be an acquired taste.

## The Four O'Clocks, Miracle of the World.

### *Mirabilis nyctaginea*

Few authorities on the subject of medicinal plants have ever paid much attention to the four o'clocks. Yet a dozen native American groups used one species or another medicinally, and some of the uses are quite unusual. At least five different groups used the root of one or another species of four o'clock as a dressing for swellings or sores. The Navajo used a cold infusion of the root of trailing four o'clock, *Allionia incarnata*, as a lotion for swellings; they also used a poultice of the mashed root of many-flowered four o'clock, *Mirabilis multiflora*, for the same purpose. The Omaha, Dakota, and Teton Sioux all used the umbrella plant, *Mirabilis nyctaginea*, for sores and swellings, making a tea or poultice of the mashed root. The Paiute similarly sprinkled the powdered root of another four o'clock, *Hermidium alipes*, on wounds to promote healing; they also made the powder into a paste for burns, or into a thin wash for impetigo. The Chippewa and Ojibwa used the umbrella plant for similar purposes, using the fresh or dried root on sprains and strained muscles.

The Dakota Indians drank a tea made by boiling the root of the same plant to reduce fevers while the Papago used a similar solution for headaches, either internally, or as a soothing compress.

These latter uses bring us to a most interesting aspect of the native American uses of the four o'clocks. I am aware of no laboratory or experimental evidence to back up this notion, but there is a tiny indication that *Mirabilis nyctaginea* may be hallucinogenic. Here is the evidence. In the 1930's, Alfred Whiting did a substantial amount of research on the uses of plants by the Hopi Indians. One of his informants, a fellow whom he identified as "Edmund," told him that the root of this species was chewed by medicine men to induce visions while making medical diagnoses. Subsequently, many authors writing about the Hopi, or about hallucinogenic plants, have repeated this as if it were true. Some have noted their source (Whiting) while some have not. Whiting listed two other species as being used for the same purpose. The

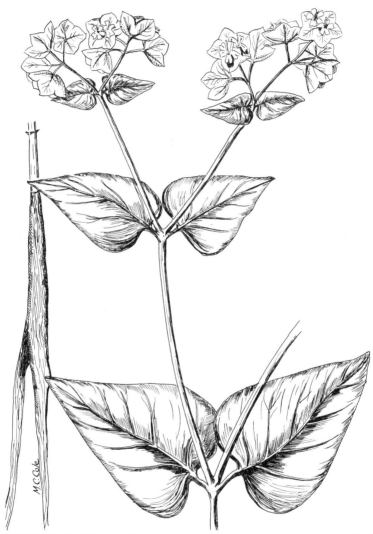

*UMBRELLA PLANT:* Mirabílis nyctaginea. *The umbrella plant is a Four O'Clock with smooth, broad, heart-shaped leaves arranged in pairs along a smooth stem. Green, five-lobed flower bracts form a saucer-like cup for the small purple or pink flowers. Four O'Clocks are one to three-foot tall plants which grow in dry soils and prairies; they flower from June to October.*

first was Jimsonweed, *Datura meteloides*, which is, no doubt, hallucinogenic, as our chapter on that plant indicates. The second was a plant called in Hopi *"pale'na"*; unfortunately, no one could find a specimen of this plant for Whiting to identify.

I have never tried chewing four o'clock roots. My one personal hallucinogenic experience with peyote in 1964 was enough to last a lifetime, and I do not indulge in such chemicals. A colleague of mine, Richard Ford, who is director of the Museum of Anthropology at the University of Michigan and a well-known ethnobotanist, has told me of some students in Arizona who, based on Whiting's writings, tried eating four o'clock; he says they experienced no particular effects.

There is little reason, then, to believe that four o'clocks are hallucinogenic. There is some reason to believe that they may have some neurological effects. I have already mentioned that the Dakota drank a tea of the plant to reduce fevers, and that the Papago used the same solution for headaches. An earlier authority on the Hopi, Walter Hough, who did his work in the 1890s, reported that the Hopi used several species of four o'clocks in similar ways. He noted that they used sand verbena, *Abronia eliptica*, multi-flowered four o'clock, and umbrella plant to induce sleep in infants. The first two were placed on the child's head to achieve this narcotic end. The latter is a bit more complicated. Hough reported that, in Hopi, this species was named for the bat and that children who would not sleep during the day were washed with a boiled tea of the plant; this would make them sleep because bats sleep during the day. This, presumably, refers to the habit of the flower which is to remain closed during the day and to open late in the day. Whiting, who asked his Hopi informants about this forty years later, says that few of them could confirm any of it. He, however, is the one who reported the notion of medicine man visions.

Another use of the four o'clocks, rather more prosaic, seems much less controversial. The Hopi regularly tie bird traps to the plant to anchor them. Few birds are capable of pulling up the long tap root of this lovely flower.

Probably the better way to enjoy visions with this plant is to forget about eating the roots in favor of watching the flowers. The common four o'clock of our gardens is a South American species, *Mirabilis Jalapa*, which was introduced into Spain in the 16th century. The brilliant flower was known as the Miracle of Peru because of its striking multicolored blooms; the English herbalist John Gerard called it the Miracle of the World! If you are tired of the same old peppermint petunias in everyone's garden, try planting some four o'clocks. I doubt that eating the roots will produce any hallucinogenic experiences (indeed, I would predict a modest cathartic effect). But watching the flowers open every afternoon will certainly be a visionary experience, and a guaranteed non-toxic one!

## Ginseng, the plant that cries.

### *Panax quinquefolium*

Few medicinal plants have received as much attention for as little reason as American ginseng. Considered in China to be the ultimate medicine, the restorer of health otherwise lost forever, belonging solely to the Emperor who could bestow it on those he favored, thought to correct all debilities of the spleen—the center of life and health—ginseng has been collected nearly to extinction. The great majority of American ginseng has been collected for sale in China, particularly ironic since the Chinese generally assert that, in its medicinal qualities, American ginseng, *Panax quinquefolium*, is far inferior to the Chinese type, *P. ginseng*. Yet American ginseng has been so intensively collected that the once-common plant is now on the Smithsonian Institution list of threatened species, in danger of extinction.

The scientific evidence for the medicinal value of American ginseng is, at best, slim. But this has been insufficient to dent the worldwide trade in the herb. In China, the root of the plant is considered to be an invaluable tonic which extends life and enhances its intensity; particularly, it is thought to increase sexual vigor. It is a "panacea," a drug used for any illness, or to enhance good health, preventing illness. Particularly potent roots are those which are shaped like the human form; in such a case, that segment of the plant resembling the part of the body implicated in illness is the most desirable.

Native Americans used ginseng, by and large, for the same purposes as the Chinese. Several tribes—the Delaware, Mohegan, Fox, and Creek—considered it a valuable panacea useful in any illness, and used it to strengthen other medicines. The Menominee used it as a tonic to strengthen mental powers. The Penobscot believed that it enhanced fertility, and the Fox, Delaware, and Mohegan considered it helpful for sexual problems and used it as a love charm. The Creek used it to scare away ghosts. Ordinarily, this concordance of interest on different continents would suggest that the plant might have demonstrably effective principles. But it

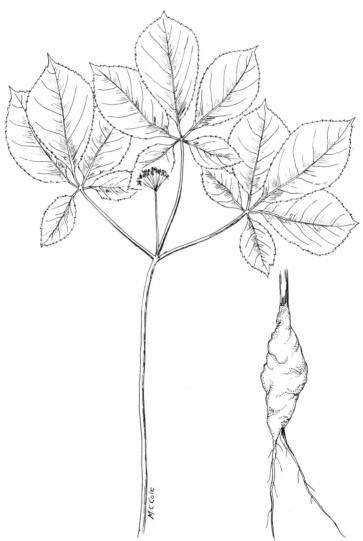

*GINSENG:* Panax quinquefolium. *A round cluster of greenish flowers rises from the axils of the three leaves. The leaves are divided into five leaflets with pointed tips. The fruits form clusters of scarlet berries. The roots of these eight to sixteen-inch plants are large and spindle-shaped. The plant grows in moist woods and flowers in June and July.*

doesn't. My own belief is that native Americans learned these uses, in effect, from the Chinese, by the intervention of traders who paid them to collect the roots for the China trade. There are some other native American uses of ginseng which seem more "indigenous." The Potawatomi used a cooled tea of the pounded roots as a soothing eyewash, and used the pounded roots topically for earaches. The Ojibwa bound the pounded root on wounds to stop bleeding and to enhance healing.

In my opinion, the preponderance of effects attributed to ginseng are due to the placebo effect. This is not to say that the effects aren't there, but it is to say that the effects are a consequence of what people *think* about the plant, and have little to do with any of its constituents. Many people, especially physicians, belittle and minimize the significance of placebo effectiveness. Many people believe that if a patient responds to a placebo—an inert drug, a starch capsule, for example—he wasn't really sick in the first place, that it was "all in his head." This attitude represents an extraordinary simplification or trivialization of the complexity of human health and illness. It also raises a curious paradox. Many people agree that the way we live, the way we think, can have a strong influence on our health. We are quick to agree with the notion that a hard-driving, aggressive and competitive "Type A" person is likely to damage his heart as a consequence of his behavior. We agree that stress can cause ulcers, that is, running sores in the gut. But when we turn the tables, and suggest that the ulcers can be healed by properly manipulating the same channels that caused them in the first place, we find that people disagree, and when such treatment succeeds, they argue that, well, he wasn't really sick in the first place. It is really a very strange situation.

I would estimate after sustained study of the problem that, in contemporary American medicine, about 30 or 40 percent of all healing which can be attributed to medicine (many things, of course, heal without medical attention) should be attributed to placebo effectiveness. That next to no research is done on how to maximize this extraordinary human healing strikes me as at best ridiculous and at worst a scandal.

It is clearly the case that if a person *believes* some medicine will help him, it will work better than if he doesn't believe it. But I ask you not to believe in ginseng. The intense belief in ginseng over the past several centuries has depleted our continent of a wonderful and unique plant, its five fingered leaves delicately fluttering, its knobby root storing up the nutrients the plant needs to survive and reproduce. If you want to use a panacea, use sweetflag as did the Micmac and Mohegan, or wild ginger like the Montagnais, or dandelions like the Navajo, or bloodroot like the Delaware and Menominee. But don't use ginseng. The Chinese say that ginseng can talk, that one finds it by listening for its imploring, mournful voice. No one has succeeded in translating the language of ginseng into Chinese or English. But if ginseng could talk, and if we could understand, I think we would hear a sad simple request to refrain from causing the extinction of the species.

## Goldenrod, "far fetcht and deare bought..."

### *Solidago canadensis*

Goldenrod is one of our most common and widespread wild-flowers. There are some 75 species of the genus *Solidago* in North America. Most regions have at least a dozen local species, and some eastern states have as many as 30. Yet, common as it is, it is often neglected. Were we to take a survey, my guess is that most people would consider the goldenrods to be weeds, not flowers. This is a shame since they are beautiful flowers, intensely yellow or gold, in enormous variety; they grow everywhere, brightening the least favored fields, waste places, and roadsides with their cheerful golden blooms. We may dismiss them, but certainly insects don't—any budding entomologist should observe goldenrods, for few other flowers attract such a range of creatures.

At least 13 different species of goldenrods were used medicinally by native Americans. They were particularly favored by the Chippewa who used a half dozen species in a whole variety of ways. They used the tall goldenrod, *Solidago altissima*, for sores or boils, applying poultices of either the moistened flowers or the pulverized root. They also used the flowers as a dressing for burns. They used a boiled root tea of *S. juncea* to stop convulsions, and boiled root tea of *S. graminifolia* for chest pains. *Solidago speciosa* was used as a compress for strains or sprains and, in a boiled root tea, as a medicine to facilitate difficult labor (the root was also mixed with bear grease to make a hair dressing!)

The Potawatomi used boiled teas of the blossoms of several different species of goldenrod to reduce fevers; the Delaware used *S. juncea* in the same way. The Thompson Indians drank a boiled tea of *S. decumbens* for a stimulating tonic as well as for venereal disease. The Hopi gave *S. petradoria* to nursing mothers to ease breast pain and to stop milk flow.

According to the great ethnobotanist Huron H. Smith, the Fox Indians say that sometimes a child does not learn how to talk or laugh. To cure such a terrible affliction, the medicine man must find the bones of an animal that died when the child was born and cook them with the leaves and flowers of the Canadian goldenrod,

*CANADA GOLDENROD:* Solidago canadensis. *In the late summers, abandoned fields and roadsides are blanketed with the tall, yellow-topped goldenrods. The one to five-foot plant has linear, toothed, tapering leaves and plume-like clusters of tiny yellow flowers. The stem is smooth at the base and becomes increasingly downy toward the top. Found in clearings, fields and roadsides.*

*Solidago canadensis*. The baby, washed with this liquid, will quickly overcome his affliction, and grow up with his faculties intact.

The fragrant goldenrod, *S. odorata*, was in the USP from 1820 until 1882, but was never very widely used. A tea made of the flowers and leaves is mildly stimulating and carminative, that is, it is one of those herbs to use after a heavy spicy dinner in place of an antacid tablet. But it is unlikely that too many people will. In the 17th century, the British herbalist John Gerard had the same story to tell. For a while, it seems, the great wonder drug of the day was a newly discovered species of goldenrod imported at great expense from Germany, so valuable as to fetch a half-crown for an ounce. But then the same herb was discovered growing in Hampstead Wood at the edge of town, and, in a trice, no one would pay a half-crown for a hundredweight, nor use it medicinally at all any more. Gerard wistfully concluded that this set of affairs demonstrated the truth of the old English proverb: "Far fetcht and deare bought is best for Ladies." One would be unlikely in this more liberated day to come to exactly that conclusion, but the point is clear enough.

HOPS: Humulus lupulus. *Hops is a twining vine characterized by large, oppositely arranged, deeply indented leaves and drooping clusters of fruits. The stem is rough and covered with stiff hairs. A native of Europe and Asia, hops escaped cultivation and may be found on river banks and in moist thickets.*

## Hops: A pillow for King George.

### *Humulus lupulus*

Most of us have consumed hops in fair quantity, though we are generally unaware of it. Hops is the ingredient in beer which gives it its bitter tang. Although today the function of hops in beer is only to provide flavoring, such was not always the case. Originally, the hops was useful in that its several antibacterial principles kept the beer from turning rancid during the brewing process. These principles probably also account for some of the native American uses of the plant as a wound dressing. The Dakota and Omaha, among others, used the hop root on wounds to aid healing. The Delaware heated a small bag of the leaves and held it on the ear for earaches, or on the gums for toothache.

But most medicinal uses of hops have been internal. The Dakota used the root tea for intestinal pains or "colic," and a tea of the fruit to reduce fever. The Navajo used a leaf tea for coughs and flu while the Ojibwa and Cherokee used a similar formulation as a diuretic and for other urinary complaints.

The most interesting and unusual use of hops, however, is as a sedative or "tranquilizer." The Delaware made a tea of the blossoms and drank a small amount several times a day for "nervousness." The Mohegan used a similar formulation to relieve nervous tensions. The Fox used the root to induce sleep for those suffering from insomnia. The Cherokee used the herb to alleviate pain, as we might use aspirin, and to induce sleep.

The plant was widely used as a sedative and tonic during the last century. The flowers were listed in the USP from 1820 until 1926. One of the more interesting historical uses of hops involved George III, the last king of America. George was not healthy. Medical historians have suggested that he suffered from porphyria, a rare inherited disorder with a number of unpleasant symptoms. One treatment his physicians used to ease his insomnia and mental suffering was to have him sleep on a pillow stuffed with hops.

It is often suggested that hops is an hallucinogen and is an effective and legal substitute for marijuana. In part this is probably due to the fact that the two species are classed together in the same family. It may also, in part, be due to a curious incident in the last century when some British merchants marketed a substance they called Hopeine which, they said, was a narcotic alkaloid derived, at great expense, from the finest wild American hops. They were quite successful with their product until someone demonstrated that it was a mixture of an aromatic oil and morphine.

In any case, while the sedative and tonic properties of hops seem certain, the hallucinogenic properties, in all likelihood, reside much more in the user than in the herb.

Hop tea or, indeed, a hop pillow, is a reasonable drug for cases of nervous insomnia. Pour hot water over a bit of hop flower, perhaps mixed half and half with camomile (a European plant widely available in herb shops), and steep for a few minutes. But, as recommended earlier, the better remedy for "nerves" is to be certain that you gather the hops yourself. Look for them in thickets, fencerows, abandoned house sites, and along road sides. The search, successful or not, will be as therapeutic as any tea.

## Indian pipes and pipsissewa, the green and white of things.

*Monotropa uniflora*

*Chimaphila umbellata*

Finding Indian pipes is one way of knowing that I have gotten there. There are other ways, like hearing the intense silence of the dusk after the birds have quieted down and before the cicadas have begun their chiming, but the Indian pipes are one of the best. To travel off to a more personal kind of life mediated more by my tools (pack, fly-rod, boots) than by my society (friends, colleagues, neighbors), is one of the ways I try to keep track of the center. It is hard to be personable if you aren't sure of your person. The Indian pipes, little parasitic flowers lacking chlorophyll, grow on the roots of trees or on thick decaying vegetation. They need a rich un-tramped woodland where no one rakes the leaves, where the trees grow tall with an unbroken canopy. They are fragile little things which grow best where no one protects them, or cleans up after them; a good metaphor for someone seeking self definition. I have found them several times, in the Adirondacks, and in Algonquian Park in Ontario. It is arresting to see them, their pale waxy-white stems holding the single nodding pink-tinged flower. No one, I assert, can casually glance at Indian pipes without stopping for a closer look. Pick one, and it will soon turn black and crumble. You must enjoy it in its place.

Few tribes used this curious plant medicinally. The Mohegan drank a boiled tea of the flower to relieve aches and pains due to colds, and the Potawatomi (perhaps employing the logic of parasitic mistletoe) used a tea of the fibrous rootlets for "female troubles." The plant was also occasionally used by native and other Americans as an eyewash; the sappy fluid squeezed from the plant was said to relieve inflamed eyes.

The Indian pipes belong to the small family Pyrolaceae which includes several other interesting species. The pinedrops, *Pterospora andromeda*, like the Indian pipes, have no chlorophyll

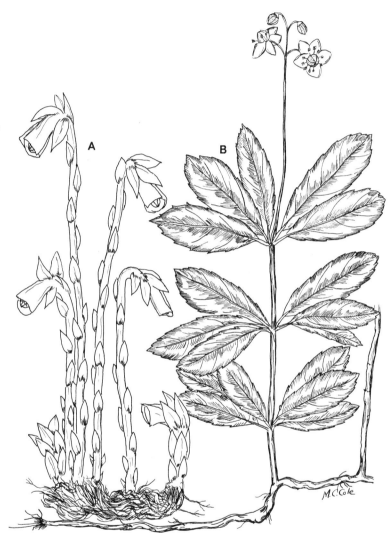

(A) *INDIAN PIPES:* Monotropa uniflora. *The unusual Indian pipes are one-flowered, translucent herbs of rich, shaded woods. They are parasitic on decomposing plant matter.*
(B) *PIPSISSEWA:* Chimaphila umbellata. *The dark green, shiny, whorled leaves of Pipsissewa have toothed margins. Pipsissewa is an evergreen plant with spreading roots that forms colonies in rich woods.*

and are parasitic. But they grow almost exclusively in dry alkaline soils under pine trees. The tall single wand-like stem, purplish-brown, holds a dozen or more nodding pink flowers—another most unusual plant. It was used medicinally by the Cheyenne Indians as an astringent to stop nose bleeds and hemorrhage of the lungs. In their rather direct style, the Cheyenne called the plant *mati minis tohisse heyo,* which literally translated, means "to bleed at the nose medicine." The stem and berries were ground up and boiled; the cooled liquid was snuffed up the nose and rubbed on the head for nose bleed, or drunk for lung hemorrhage. This is the only medicinal use of this plant I have encountered. The third parasitic member of this family is sweet pinesap or pigmy-pipes, *Monotropsis odorata,* which looks much like Indian pipe but with three or four "pipe-bowl" flowers rather than only one. To my knowledge, it has never been used medicinally.

Other members of the family are more usual plants, with chlorophyll, not parasitic. The most widely used of these was pipsissewa, *Chimaphila umbellata.* The name pipsissewa is apparently of Algonquian origin but the precise etymology or source of the word is not clear. Both the Menominee and the Thompson Indians found this to be a particularly useful drug for women during childbirth. Thompson Indian women chewed the plant or drank a warm tea of the leaves during childbirth to ease pain. Menominee women added the plant to a number of other formulations for their particular problems to make them taste good; they added it, in particular, to a complex compound drug used after childbirth to aid internal healing.

Three different groups, the Delaware, Mohegan and Penobscot, applied a tea of the leaves to blisters to help heal them. The Chippewa used the boiled root tea as an eye wash while the Ojibwa used the leaf tea for stomach aches. The dried leaves were a highly favored smoking "tobacco" of the Blackfoot. A closely related species, the single-flowered pyrola, *Moneses uniflora,* was taken by the Montagnais in cases of paralysis and was applied to swellings by the Kwakiutl.

Several other species in this family, all called "wintergreen," have been used medicinally. They should not be confused with another wintergreen, *Gaultheria procumbens,* which belongs to a different, although closely related, family (see our chapter on Black Birch and Wintergreen). One of these "wintergreens," *Pyrola asarifolia*, also known as shinleaf (for what reason I cannot imagine!) was considered to be a particularly useful medicine by the Montagnais who took it for any ailment at all as a general strengthener. The Carrier Indians used this and another, *P. secunda*, as an eyewash.

Another of these wintergreens, *P. elliptica*, is also called canker leaf. The Mohegan used boiled leaf tea as a wash for canker sores while the Nootka are said to have applied the bruised leaves to "tumors," though this may refer as well to cankers and not to the cancerous lesions we associate with the word. The Nanticoke used spotted wintergreen, *Chimaphila maculata*, to reduce fevers.

Pipsissewa was listed in the USP from 1820 until 1916 and was widely used as a tonic and astringent. The other species have not been official, but have found use as home remedies over the centuries.

But, as I have indicated, my heart in this case belongs not to officialdom, but to Indian pipes. I consider them one of the most useful psychiatric drugs—certainly not to ingest (I've never been able even to go so far as to pick one, it would seem like murder), but only to be in their company. One never sleeps better than when he knows he is in the neighborhood of Indian pipes.

### Jack-in-the-pulpit, or "memory root."

*Arisaema triphyllum*

*Arisaema dracontium*

Jack-in-the-pulpit is one of the most unusual of wildflowers. The little spadix, "Jack," stands surrounded by a spathe, his "pulpit," which extends up and over his head forming a green or purple canopy. In the fall, his pulpit has fallen away, and Jack has produced a clump of rather nasty looking scarlet berries. The Iroquois, not having traditions of either pulpits or the name "Jack," call this little flower "cradleboard," no less appropriate.

For a number of native American groups, Jack-in-the-pulpit was considered to be a particularly powerful and magical plant. The Fox, for instance, used it in a divination rite to predict the course of illness. One of those nasty looking berries was stripped of its pulp, exposing the seed which was dropped in a cup of swirling water. If the seed floated around the surface four times, the patient would recover. If it sank, the patient would die.

Among the Menominee, one indication that someone had been subjected to witchcraft was that his mouth would appear crooked, pulled to one side. When this occurred, the dried root of Jack-in-the-pulpit was finely pulverized with the root of the closely related sweetflag; the powder was inserted into a tiny incision made in the lip to counteract the witchery and straighten the mouth.

The Iroquois considered the plant to be so powerful that it could not be kept in the house near other medicines; to do so would contaminate and spoil them. If one were to collect some "cradleboard" too early in the spring, before it was ready to be picked, it could cause you to go blind.

There were other more commonplace uses of Jack-in-the-pulpit. Two tribes used the plant to relieve headaches. The Pawnee dried and crumbled the root and sprinkled the powder on the head and temples. The Cherokee held the raw root on the head or temples. Similarly, both the Mohegan and Penobscot used a boiled root tea as a liniment for sore muscles and joints.

The Chippewa, Menominee and Iroquois all used the plant to

(A) *JACK-IN-THE-PULPIT*: Arisaema triphyllum. *The fruiting head of flowers (spadix) is enclosed by a striped purple-brown or green hoos (spathe). Leaves are arranged at the ends of slender stalks. In the fall, scarlet berries form. The plant is found in thickets and wet, rich woods.*

(B) *GREEN DRAGON*: Arisaema dracontium. *Green dragon differs by having a single leaf divided into five to fifteen leaflets and a long, tapered spadix. Green dragon is almost always found on flood plains along rivers.*

relieve sore eyes. The Chippewa bathed the eyes with boiled root tea while the Menominee used the fresh ground roots as a poultice. The Iroquois boiled the roots and put the eyes over the steam. The Ojibwa used the root of the closely related "green dragon," *Arisaema dracontium*, in a similar manner.

Probably because the root of the Jack-in-the-pulpit is so terribly bitter (some say that it is called "memory root" because you will never forget the experience if you taste it!) few of these uses are internal. The Mohegan gargled a very dilute boiled root tea for sore throats, and the Choctaw drank a similar formulation as a tonic to "make blood." But these are clearly the exception.

Under these circumstances, it seems particularly strange that a number of native American groups as well as other peoples around the world, used various *Arisaema* species, at least occasionally, as food. To make the acrid roots edible, dig a hole, fill it with the roots, and roast them by building a fire over them. Though I have never tried this, they are said to be very appetizing. Among others, the roots were eaten this way by the Shawnee and the Iroquois. Another name for the green dragon is "Indian turnip," indicating its dietary role. Other species are reportedly prepared much the same way and eaten by the Ainu of Japan, and by various native peoples in the Himalayas and Nepal.

Jack-in-the-pulpit was listed in the USP from 1820 until 1873; it was used medicinally as a stimulant and expectorant, though it was never a highly favored remedy.

If you have the right conditions—a shady cool spot with thick organic soil—Jack-in-the-pulpit can be cultivated. It is such an extraordinary and unusual plant that it is well worth the effort. Transplant wild plants by digging them up with a large ball of dirt (basketball size) trying not to disturb the roots. Keep them moist, and mulch them well in the fall with leaves or peat moss. The Jack-in-the-pulpit cannot be called beautiful, but it is certainly *striking*, and, as such, is well worth growing. I have not yet succeeded in propagating them from seeds, but I will keep trying.

The Jack-in-the-pulpit is, as well, a fascinating target for your camera, not flashy, not even really pretty, but interesting and unusual. What is involved in photographing flowers? For the moderately equipped photographer, wild flowers, medicinal or otherwise, are a marvelous subject. I have been photographing them for 20 years, and my collection includes pictures from all over North America. As I look at them with friends, I am afraid I become awfully boorish—it is extraordinary how a beautiful photograph of a field of rich golden vetches, framed by the "Flatirons" outside Boulder, Colorado, can bring back a whole constellation of memories of that crystal day 12 years ago as my wife and I tromped through fields and woods in those magnificent Rocky Mountain foothills. That was the day we met a wizened little man—a professor of entomology at the University of Colorado—who let us walk along with him as he, swishing a little butterfly net back and forth, captured dozens of the miniscule indigenous bees which were his professional passion. He talked quietly and lovingly for an hour about the many kinds of bees, each specialized to feed on one or a few specific species of flowers. I recall particularly his scorn at the imported European honey bee—buzz bombers I believe he called them, nuclear bomb bees—which took over the feeding space of his beloved native bees. It was one of those enchanting experiences that one never forgets. But I always actually *remember* it when I see that picture of the yellow vetch framed by the Flatirons. How *many* of my pictures recall a similar memory! The softly focused blue iris which always reminds me of the two baby coyotes chasing butterflies in the same Black Hills meadow; the Indian paintbrush along the mountain stream where I caught my largest trout; on and on the stories come, to the point where, I fear, my audience drifts off—I am left alone for the last few, the fields of South Carolina marsh grass where we saw the ospreys fishing, the ice plant near the Pacific tide pools where the spiny lobsters hid beneath blue mussels, on and on.

The key to photographing flowers is to *get close*, as close as you can. You need a single-lens reflex camera, 35 millimeter. A macro-lens which focuses to an inch or so is best; lacking that expensive option, extension tubes or supplementary close-up lenses are acceptable substitutes (I use close-up lenses; a good set costs about $20). Any moderate speed color film, with an ASA speed of 150 to 200 is fine for flowers; slides or prints are both fine as well depending on your preference—I use both. To get close, you usually have to get right down on the ground on your belly. To take a picture of a may apple, your camera lens has to be below the nodding leaf to capture the creamy flower which is perhaps 6 or 8 inches above the ground. This is typical (kinnikinik is a *particular* challenge)! Watch for flowers attracting bees or butterflies for particularly interesting pictures. The best time of day for flower pictures is when the sun is low in the sky, early in the morning or late in the evening. The quality of such low light suffuses wild flowers with a soft golden glow.

The hardest thing to control with such pictures is the background. Before you click the shutter be sure to check the surrounding view. The flower may look properly framed, but if the horizon is slanted the picture will be ruined. With such severe close-ups, depth of field or depth of focus is often very small, a few inches perhaps. Sometimes this is very desirable—a blossom, crystal clear, surrounded by the subtle glow of a dozen others only hinting at their presence by washes of color can be truly striking. In strong light, focusing on a flower a foot or so away from the lens, it is possible with a small aperture to have an infinite horizon in focus as well. There was the day near Aspen when some sunflowers stood framed by a snow-capped saddle between two peaks. We were camped along a creek, and rummaging around, we had found three graves, topped by wooden crosses made of sticks...but there I go again.

You need not travel far to photograph flowers. There are substantial advantages in working close to home. On a Tuesday evening, you find a rich collection of Jack-in-the-pulpits. The light is perfect, but the leaves aren't quite unfolded yet. So wait a day or two or a week, and return to the same spot. They will still be there. But the light may not be right. Wait another few days and try again. But by then, when the light is right again, those beautiful nearby trillium, which were to frame your photo, have dropped their petals. Take the picture anyway. And go back again next year, and try again. This is the ultimate advantage of photographing close to home. Those little cradleboards are worth the wait.

(**A**) *JIMSONWEED:* Datura stamonium. *The coarse-looking one to ten-foot tall poisonous Jimson-weeds have large leaves and green-purple stems. The pale violet to white flowers are three to five inches long. Spiny seed pods give this plant of abandoned fields and waste places a sinister appearance.*
(**B**) *JIMSONWEED:* Datura meteloides. *The sommth broad leaves of* Datura meteloides *distinguish it from* Datura stramonium, *which has jagged leaf edges.*

## Jimsonweed, the devil's apple

*Datura stramonium*

*Datura meteloides*

Jimsonweed, also known as thorn apple, devil's apple, and mad apple, is without doubt *the most dangerous plant we will consider in this book*. The plant contains several very powerful hypnotic and hallucinogenic alkaloids, any of which is even quite modest doses can be fatal. The plant has played a fascinating role in both American and European cultures and will be described for that reason. But, beware; playing with *Datura* is playing with the hottest kind of fire.

Now, paradoxically, I am going to note that the most common use of this plant around the world has been as a rather humble ointment for healing sores and recalcitrant ulcers. The Delaware used the seeds and leaves as a coagulant in wounds, the Mohegan used the crushed leaves as a poultice on cuts, the Zuni sprinkled powdered root and flowers into wounds to promote healing, and the Cherokee used the wilted leaves as a poultice for boils. The Coahuilla of California used the crushed leaves to heal saddle sores on their horses. Similarly, Gerard, in his herbal, noted that an ointment made of the juice of thorn apple boiled with lard cured "all inflammations whatsoever," and was particularly effective on burns. And in China, *Datura* has long been used as a wash for facial eruptions, swollen feet, and for hemorrhoids.

I am unaware of any pharmacological investigations of this aspect of the daturas, and to suggest which principles have appropriate antibacterial or anti-inflammatory action would be pure speculation. Those who have examined the genus closely have been far more interested in its narcotic and hallucinatory qualities, regarding which the available information is enormous.

Daturas of one species or another have been used as hypnotics and narcotics, sometimes alone, sometimes in combination with other drugs, in many different places. One stronghold is the American west and southwest, continuing south into Mexico. The

Hopi used *Datura meteloides,* sometimes referred to as *D. inoxia,* in two ways. First, the Hopi medicine man confronted with a sick person would chew the roots. This induced visions which were interpreted to determine the cause of the sufferer's illness. Second, it was sometimes used as a stimulant of sorts to perk up sick people, but there was much controversy about this use, and some evidence of fatal results, expecially when prescribed for children.

Among the Zuni, in addition to its use on wounds, *Datura* was used as an anesthetic before surgical procedures, such as setting broken bones or cleaning infected wounds. Similarly, the Navajo used *Datura* as a narcotic to control pain from serious injuries, but, recognizing its poisonous nature, they handled it very carefully.

Several southwestern tribes used *Datura* less for its narcotic than for its hallucinatory qualities. Among these were the Apache who added ground *Datura* root to corn beer to "make heaven and earth meet." This brew induced strong visions which were the basis for prophesy. The Aztecs of Mexico used *Datura,* which they called "toloatzin," as an hallucinogen as well as for the skin disorders and wounds mentioned earlier. Until recently, most scholars thought that the Aztec visionary plant called "ololiuqui" was also *Datura,* but subsequently this plant has been identified as a kind of morning glory, *Rivea corymbosa,* the seeds of which contain a series of alkaloids very similar to LSD. The hallucinogenic qualities of morning glories were only discovered by Western scientists in the late 1940s; this combined with the similar trumpet shape of the flowers of morning glory and *Datura,* probably accounts for the confusion. Indeed, some have argued that the flowers represented on the "squash blossom" necklaces of the Zuni are really Daturas.

The most extensive use of the hallucinogenic qualities of *Datura* occurred on the East and West Coasts of North America. Both the Algonquian Indians of Virginia, and several tribes from California, particularly the Luiseño of the San Diego area and the Yokuts of the San Jaoquin valley, used the plant as part of an intense and dramatic initiation ceremony for young boys. In all three of these groups at irregular intervals of several years an initiation was held for all the boys who had come of age, between about 12 and 17 years old, since the last ceremony. After appropriate rituals, the boys were given *Datura* tea. Among the California tribes, the intoxication lasted from one to four or five days. In Virginia, the boys were repeatedly fed the tea, calley "wysoccan," remaining in a drugged state for as long as 18 or 20 days. This Virginia ritual is quite extraordinary since the early accounts of it suggest that the purpose was to completely destroy the initiates memory of childhood. They were presumed to have forgotten everything—even how to speak. They had then to relearn everything, this time as men not boys. Initiation rituals around the world are often structured as second births, but this is the most extreme case I have ever encountered. It is not clear if the amnesia was "real" or not, but is seems clear enough that it was meaningful!

*Datura* was also an important hallucinogen during the Middle Ages in Europe where, according to Anthropologist Michael Harner of the New School for Social Research, it was one of several ingredients used in "witchcraft salves." These salves were complicated compounds which included, among other things, the deadly nightshade, *Atropa belladonna*, the mandrake, *Mandragora officinaum*, henbane, *Hyoscamus niger*, and *Datura*. All of these species contain the hallucinogenic or narcotic alkaloids atropine, hyoscamine and scopalomine in varying proportions. Atropine is particularly important since it can be absorbed through the skin; these salves were generally applied to the wrist and forehead. A common element in European witchcraft, familiar to all children at Halloween, is the witch flying on her broomstick. Harner has suggested that the basis for this notion is that the witches coated a stick with their ointment, and then rubbed it on the sensitive vaginal membranes. Since there is some evidence that these alkaloids often induce visions of flying (or at least a feeling of vertigo which is interpreted as flying), this practice would probably account for the curious combination of flight and intense sexuality characteristic of the European witch tradition.

Jimsonweed is a member of the most unusual plant family, the Solanaceae, This family contains many other hallucinogenic species including not only the nightshade, henbane, and mandrake already mentioned, but also several hallucinogenic South American genera like *Brunfelsia*, *Cestrum*, and *Iochroma*; but in addition to these extraordinary plants, the family also includes the tomato, *Lycopersicon esculentum*, the potato, *Solanum tuberosum*, the chili pepper, *Capsicum spp.*, tobacco, *Nicotiana*, and (would you believe) petunias.

Jimsonweed was long used by physicians. The plant was listed in the USP from 1820 until 1950, and several of the alkaloids are still widely used in medicine as analgesic pain killers and sedatives. Until quite recently, scopalomine was combined with morphine and used during childbirth to induce "twilight sleep," a state of dulled consciousness or enhanced amnesia; this procedure occasionally resulted in asphyxiation of the infant, and is no longer practiced.

*Datura* and its related hallucinogens are extremely dangerous drugs. The quantity of alkaloids varies from species to species, from season to season, and from plant to plant, so one rarely knows in advance how large a dose he is getting. *Datura* is rarely found except around human habitations where it grows in garbage dumps and manure piles—the largest plant I have ever seen, eight or nine feet tall, was in the barnyard of a friend's home in the hill country of Southern Ohio.

It should be clear enough that I do not recommend that anyone should ever ingest any of the Daturas. In fact, if you find some, I would urge you to give it a wide berth—if you have a sore that needs healing, look for some sumac. This course has its own dangers, but you won't find yourself flying on a broomstick, a most unreliable mode of transportation. Broomsticks crash, and so do people who eat *Datura*.

## Joe Pye weed and boneset.

*Eupatorium purpureum*

*Eupatorium perfoliatum*

Joe Pye, the story goes, was an Indian from somewhere in New England who gained fame by curing typhus with *Eupatorium purpureum*; consuming the plant caused sufferers to break out in a heavy sweat which broke the fever and saved the day. The plant has been known as Joe Pye (or Jopi) weed ever since.

The genus is a complicated one with 35 or 40 North American species, many of them more or less indiscriminately called boneset, thoroughwort, gravel root, ague weed, fever weed, Indian sage, and, for reasons which remain obscure, queen-of-the-meadow. These names, most of them indicating some medicinal use or other, are a measure of the high esteem in which the plant was held for many such purposes.

Many tribes used various *Eupatorium* species for fevers. For example, the Menominee, Mohegan, Delaware, and Nanticoke all used boneset, *E. perfoliatum*, for fevers, drinking teas of the whole plant, or leaves, or root. The Houma used woman's head, *E. serotinum*, in much the same way. The Navajo used a cooled tea of thoroughwort, *E. herbaceum*, for fever and headache, by having the patient bathe with and drink the liquid. The Zuni used thoroughwort in the same manner for rheumatism.

Boneset was also used for a variety of other purposes. The Fox drank boiled leaf tea for intestinal parasites, the Mohegan drank leaf tea for colds, and the Delaware considered the leaf tea to be particularly effective for stomach aches.

Boneset, *E. perfoliatum*, was widely, even universally, adopted for similar uses, particularly for fevers and colds, by immigrant Europeans. It was listed in the USP from 1820 to 1916 and remained in the NF until 1950. Taking a cup of boneset tea was perhaps the 19th century equivalent of "take aspirin, drink lots of liquids, and stay in bed," the standard 20th century cold remedy. In any but the mildest concentrations, however, boneset can act as a powerful

(A) *JOE PYE WEED*: Eupatorium purpureum. *Joe Pye weed is a one to five-foot tall plant with whitish, purple-stems. The stem branches near the top to support flattened heads of small, purple flowers. The plant is found in pastures and on the banks of ditches.*

(B) *BONESET*: Eupatorium perfoliatum. *Boneset, another plant of pastures, waste places and ditches, has similar heads of small, white flowers. The stems appear to pierce the united bases of the oppositely arranged, tapered leaves. The plants are one to three feet tall.*

emetic, which will render the patient extremely nauseous and can cause intense vomiting, so if you want to try it, do so with discretion. Joe Pye weed, *E. purpureum*, was never in as great favor as boneset, but it was in the USP from 1820 until 1842; it has similar effects.

Other *Eupatorium* species also had some household uses. Dog-fennel, *E. capillifolium*, was widely used to stop the pain or itch of bee stings or insect bites. The crumbled fresh leaves were rubbed on the bite or sting. This is still a well known practice among rural inhabitants of South Carolina. Also, is is said that the foliage of this plant, strewn on the floor, will repel insects. Dog-fennel has only a superficial resemblance to the European fennel, *Foeniculum vulgare*, which is widely used now in the kitchen, and which is an essential ingredient in Italian sausage.

One must conclude with one last bit of technical ethnographic data. One Fox Indian name for Joe Pye weed is to be literally translated as "love medicine to be nibbled when speaking to women when they are in the wooing mood." Make of this what you will...

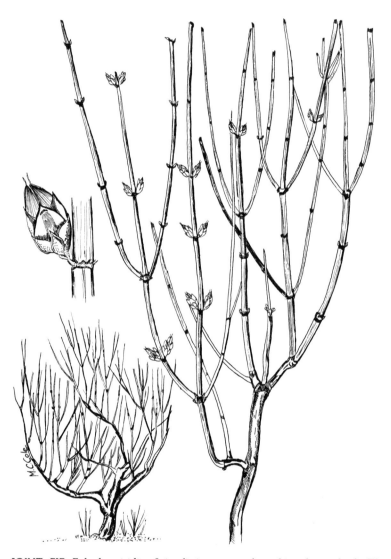

*JOINT FIR:* Ephedra viridis. *Joint fir is an erect, branching desert shrub. The many slender, yellow-green branches have two very small leaf scales at each node. The mature, double seeded cones are conspicuous in the fall. The one and a half to four-foot shrubs grow on dry slopes.*

## Joint fir, Teamster's tea, and *Ma Huang.*

### *Ephedra viridis*

This curious, leafless plant is found in desert regions in the southwestern United States. It was a favored remedy among southwestern tribes for venereal diseases. The Zuni, Pima, Hopi, Paiute, and Shoshone all used the plant this way. In most cases, a boiled tea of the branches was taken internally. In some communities, the medicine was made by combining ephedra with other plants, among them scarlet gilia, *Gilia aggregata,* and creosote bush, *Larrea divaricata.*

The plant has other uses as well. The boiled tea was used by the Tewa, Paiute, and Shoshone as an antidiarrheal, by the Paiute as an antirheumatic, by the Shoshone as a burn dressing, and by both the Paiute and Shoshone as a cold remedy and for kidney and bladder disorders.

The most interesting use of ephedra, however, comes from China. The first record of the medicinal use of Ma Huang, probably *Ephedra viridis,* dates from approximately 2800 BC when the Emperor Shen Nung is reputed to have written the first pharmocopoeia. Now Shen Nung was, by all accounts, quite a fellow. He learned to talk by the age of three days, and he could walk after one week. He plowed his first field at the age of three, not bad when we realize that he had first to invent the plow. In addition to inventing agriculture, he also domesticated the ox, and invented the yoke for horses. His name is roughly translated into English as "Divine Husbandman." Some say he had the body of a man, but the head of a bull. Shen Nung classed Ma Huang as a medicine of medium strength; it was used for millenia in China as a fever-reducer, circulatory stimulant, and cough medicine.

The world would have to wait for four or five thousand years for scientists to closely examine ephedra. In the 1920's, K.K. Chen and Carl F. Schmidt, at the Laboratory of Pharmacology of Peking Medical College, discovered that the active ingredient in ephedra, called ephedrine, was a strong stimulant to the sympathetic nervous system. The drug causes constriction of blood vessels, rise in blood pressure, dilation of the pupils, and relaxation of the intestinal and bronchial muscles. These effects are similar to those produced by a related chemical, epinephrine, better known as adrenaline, produced by the adrenal glands.

There are several contemporary medical uses of ephedrine. Its most common use is to relieve nasal congestion—it is a common constituent in cold tablets. It is also used in cases of emphysema, and, in the form of eyedrops, to dilate the pupils or, in lesser concentration, to relieve eye irritations from allergic reactions or chemical irritations. A related chemical, epinephrine hydrate, has been used as an astringent and hemostat, that is, an agent to reduce bleeding and aid healing.

Most plant scientists say that the American species of *Ephedra* have only insignificant quantities of ephedrine. The crude drug today is imported from India and Pakistan, or it is produced synthetically. But the uses of native species by southwestern Indians (as cold remedy, burn dressing, antidiarrheal, hemostat, etc.) suggest that the native plant may have enough to do the job. American settlers in the West used the herb as a stimulating tea, much as we today use coffee or "tea." Among other common names, the various species are still referred to as Teamster's tea, Mormon tea, and desert tea, reflecting this usage. To make such a tea, pour boiling water over a small bunch of broken stems, and let it steep for five or ten minutes. The tea may be drunk hot or cold.

Large doses of ephedrine can be very uncomfortable, causing nervousness, insomnia, headache, vertigo, nausea, and vomiting. Some suggest that in such large doses, the drug produces hallucinations and delirium. Others have recommended the drug as a recreational hallucinogen for these reasons. If it is hallucinogenic, then it is probably the only such plant which, in addition to causing headache, nausea and vomiting, will clear up your stuffed sinuses!

## Juniper, the gin berry.

### *Juniperus communis*

The word "gin" is very interesting. According to the Oxford Un-abridged Dictionary, it means, among other things, skill or in-genuity, cunning or contrivance, a mechanical gadget or device (as in cotton gin), a tool, a spring, a snare or other contraption for catching game, an engine of torture as the rack, a machine in warfare for casting stones, a device for securing a door like a latch, a crane for lifting weights, a female Australian aborigine, a female kangaroo, a female ferret, and the verb "did" as a form of "begin." It is also, of course, the name of the clear liquor used in martinis and mixed with tonic. The word in its mechanical senses (racks, snares) is derived from the Old English word for "engine." The Australian meanings (female humans and kangaroos) are apparently derived from a native dialect word for woman, while the term for female ferret is derived from the appellative use of the woman's name Jenny or Ginny. The name for the spirituous liquor is derived from the Dutch name for the spirit, *Geneva*, derived from Dutch *genever*, a corruption of the French *genièvre*, derived from the Latin *juniperus*. Juniperus, genievre, geneva, gin. (The card game was named "gin" as a sort of pun on the name of the game on which it is based, rummy; no one seems to know how rummy got its name!)

Gin was invented by a Dutch physician in the 17th century. He distilled juniper berries with alcohol in order to produce an in-expensive substitute for juniper berry oil, a drug considered in those days to be a valuable diuretic. Little did he know! Not wishing to consider in detail the health consequences of gin in three centuries, I am consoled that the initial motive was to extend health, at least as it was understood at the time. Juniper berries have been recognized as a diuretic (among other things) in the West for several thousand years according to the testimony of Pliny, Dioscorides, and Galen.

Several native American groups concurred. The Tewa, Paiute, Iroquois, Shoshone, and Thompson Indians all used the berries as a diuretic, either eaten raw or in a boiled tea. But this hardly

*COMMON JUNIPER:* Juniperus communis. *This low, spreading shrub has one-third to one-half inch flat leaves with silvery bands on their undersides. The leaves grow in whorls of three. Blue, round, fleshy cones are produced. Planted as ornamentals, these plants have escaped to rocky soils and dry prairies.*

exhausted the uses of this highly popular remedy. Six different species of juniper were used at least a hundred ways by two dozen American Indian groups. The Paiute of Nevada particularly favored the Utah juniper, *Juniperus osteosperma*, which they used in a wide variety of ways. They used a boiled tea of the twigs as a blood tonic, a cold, cough, and fever remedy, an antiseptic wash for cuts or sores, to relieve stomach aches, and to cure venereal disease. They drank the boiled berry tea for rheumatism, as a blood tonic, and for menstrual cramps. They inhaled the fumes of the burning twigs for headaches and colds, and used the branches in their sweat baths to relieve rheumatism and congestion from heavy colds. The Shoshone used the tree in much the same way; in addition, they used the needles as a poultice for toothaches and berry tea as a heart medicine.

Other tribes used the plant similarly. The Ojibwa, Dakota, Omaha, Pawnee, and Carrier used juniper for headaches and colds, the Hopi, Chippewa, Delaware, and Creek used it for rheumatism, and the Bella Coola and Carrier used it as a cough medicine. The Tewa, Zuni, Hopi, Delaware and several others used various teas of the leaves or berries to ease childbirth. Several plains tribes—the Pawnee, Omaha, and Dakota—used a boiled tea of berries and leaves to relieve coughs in their horses.

Various juniper species were official from 1820 until the end of the century. They were recommended as diuretics, carminatives and stimulants. A hot tea made by covering a small handful of juniper branches with a cup of cold water, then boiling for four or five minutes, is a pleasant amber color and has a mild spicy flavor.

The highest and best contemporary use of juniper, however, is in cookery. Adding a tablespoon of juniper berries to any boiled marinade for beef, rabbit, or game yields a stew beyond compare. Many suburban yards will yield their own juniper and berries as several varieties are common and extremely hardy shrubs planted around foundations and on banks.

And there is, of course, always gin.

*LADY'S SLIPPER:* Cypripedium acaule. *The inflated, yellow moccasin-shaped lip gives this striking orchid the common name of Yellow Lady's Slipper. The sepals and petals are a bronze color, and lateral petals are twisted into a spiral shape. The upright, one to two-foot high stems bear three to five lily-like leaves. The plant is found in swamps, bogs and rocky places.*

## Lady's slippers and other Orchids.

### Cypripedium calceolus

The orchid family is, by some accounts, the largest plant family in the world with as many as 800 genera and 35,000 species. North Americans have small chance to see this incredible variety since the family is primarily tropical—there are in North America only about 170 species, less than one half of one percent of all those forms.

Aside from the intense fascination people have with the flowers of orchids, only one species of all those thousands has been economically important, *Vanilla plantifolia*, which produces the long seed pods which contain vanilla, the single most important flavoring in contemporary cuisine.

Orchids display an incredible variety of modifications to insure their cross-fertilization by insects, birds, flies or other creatures. Indeed, the great naturalist Charles Darwin wrote one of his most interesting (and readable) books on the subject; *The Various Contrivances by which Orchids are Fertilized by Insects* was originally published in 1862, shortly after the publication of *On the Origin of Species* (1859). The primary argument in *Orchids* is, in effect, to show how natural selection works—in detail, in one complex and fascinating case. Says Darwin in conclusion,

> The more I study nature, the more I become impressed with ever-increasing force, that the contrivances and beautiful adaptations slowly acquired through each part occasionally varying in a slight degree but in many ways, with the preservation of those variations which were beneficial to the organism under complex and ever-varying conditions of life, transcend in an incomparable manner the contrivances and adaptations which the most fertile imagination of man could invent. (2nd revised edition, 1877.)

He is surely correct.

Although the ancient Europeans found little medicinal virtue in orchids, native Americans made use of a number of species, and one in particular, the lady's slipper, made its way into Western medicine for a century or so before it was surpassed by more modern medicines. At least one tribe, the Penobscot, used the pink lady's slipper, *Cypripedium acaule*, to make what we would now call a tranquilizer—they used a boiled tea of the whole plant to treat "nervousness." Two related species, *Cypripedium parviflorum* and *C. pubescens*, were listed in the USP from 1863 to 1916 and in the NF from 1916 until 1936 as antispasmodics or "nervines," and were used in cases diagnosed as "hysteria." These plants were considered a highly acceptable substitute for the European valerian, *Valeriana officinalis*, the other favorite tranquilizer of the times. The lady's slipper became widely known by the common name "nerve root."

But native Americans seem not to have felt much need for tranquilizers. (It is a curious comment on our times that the tranquilizer diazepam—i.e., Valium—has recently been displaced from its position as the leading American drug by cimetidine—i.e., Tagamet—which is used to treat ulcers; a quarter billion dollars worth were sold in 1980.) So they found other, more humble, uses for the charming medicinal orchids.

The Chippewa found the lady's slippers to be useful for treating indigestion, inflammations, and toothaches. The Menominee, in a rather rare show of evenhandedness, used the yellow lady's slippers, *Cypripedium arietinum*, for "female disorders," and the pink lady's slipper, *C. acaule*, for "male disorders." They also included the former in medicine bundles in order to induce dreams of the supernatural.

The Shoshone and Paiutes used the coralroot, *Corallorhiza maculata*, another orchid, to treat patients with pneumonia, believing that it would build up their blood. And two orchids were used as love medicines. The Fox mixed the showy lady's slipper with several other ingredients for this purpose, while Ojibwa men contrived to slip the root of the rein-orchis, *Habenaria viridis*, into their intended lover's food; this was considered a most reprehensible form of behavior, but, apparently, it *did* happen occasionally.

The most valuable contemporary medicinal purpose for wild orchids is much the same as that for other plants with "tranquilizing principles" which we have considered. "Bogtrotting" for orchids, as aficionados call it, is one of those activities—like flyfishing for trout or photographing hawks—which combines an intense physical activity with a focused purpose, coordinating mental and physical activity so completely, that the whole system is retuned at a new level of performance. It shares the benefits of jogging and meditation, adding another element which might be called exhilarating exhaustion. Read Darwin before you go.

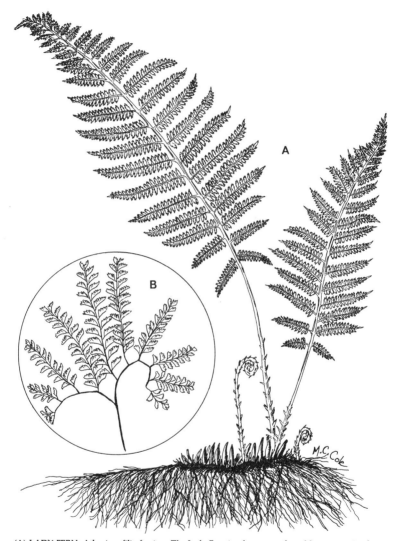

**(A)** *LADY FERN:* Athyrium filix-femina. *The Lady Fern is a large erect fern. Mature tapering leaves are about 30 inches long and ten inches wide. The flat leaf stalk is scaly at the base. The thick rhizome supports clamps of ferns in moist woods, fields and meadows.*
**(B)** *MAIDENHAIR FERN:* Adiantum pedatum. *The delicate Maidenhair fern has circular fronds on slender, 20 inch black stalks. Each semi circle has about six leaflets, each divided into fan-shaped subleaflets. They are found in rich, shaded woods and on moist banks.*

## Lady Fern, Maidenhair Fern, and "Swizzlebush."

### *Athyrium filix-femina*

### *Adiantum pedatum*

Native Americans used ferns as medicines in much the same way as they used other plants. In our family, however, ferns have a very special place.

The lady fern, *Athyrium filix-femina*, was used by the Bella Coola to make an eyewash, by the Chippewa to make a diuretic, by the Ojibwa to make a powder for healing sores, and by the Tlingit for coughs and chest pains. The Potawatomi, Fox and Ojibwa used boiled tea of the lady fern root one way or another for nursing mothers—to reduce breast pain, or to enhance milk flow. The Ojibwa used sensitive fern, *Onoclea sensibilis*, this way, and the Menominee used brake fern, *Pteridium aquilinum*, and maidenhair fern, *Adiantum pedatum*, for the same problems.

The Navajo used both brittle fern, *Cystopteris fragilis*, and Mexican woodsia, *Woodsia mexicana*, for bathing injuries, while the Eskimo used shield fern, *Dryopteris dilatata*, for stomach aches or colic.

Although none of the American ferns were ever official drugs, the European male fern, *Aspidium filix-mas*, was in the USP from 1831 until 1965, and was widely used as a medicine for tape worms.

My own experience with lady fern was rather different from these. I learned a very important lesson about medicine with a fern one day, and have, in a sense, been pursuing the issue ever since.

A beautiful river which I shall call the Magontehon rises in the Algonquian Plateau and, with several others, tumbles across Central Ontario toward Georgian Bay on Lake Huron. The rich amber color of the water is a reminder of the deep peaty woods where the river begins. Long sinuous stretches are separated by bounding rapids and chutes; it is a wonderful river for canoe trips with convenient crossroads and intense wilderness. The river is full of smallmouth bass, walleyes, and pike.

Although it is suited to much more rugged adventures, this was to be a family outing. My wife and daughter and I with my brother and his wife and daughter, were camped on a lovely peninsula. The girls, both about eight years old, shared a tent furnished with those essentials of any camping trip, sleeping bags, flash lights, and teddy bears.

The grown-ups more or less took turns with the kids. Tom was off fishing, Marquisa and Elena had gone for a walk, and it was my day with the girls. We got in the canoe, dressed in bathing suits and sneakers, and paddled upstream to a little cove below a chute where we could swim, catch frogs, and chase butterflies. It was a beautiful day—warm, blue sky, glowing sun. I, lizard-like, baked in the sun. The girls, young gazelles, rambled about. Unfortunately, one of the gazelles stumbled. Andrea, my niece, chasing a frog—her eight year old passion was for catching frogs, dozens of them, tree frogs, bull frogs, fat toads , even, on occasion, skinny toads—slipped on a rock and fell, her 56 pounds landing on her kneecap. Now that odd bone, it seems, is well endowed with sensory nerves. It didn't look as if anything was broken, but the knee was bleeding, and the poor kid was in terrible pain. Our well stocked first aid kit was, of course, back in camp. The tears were flowing, and something had to be done.

I quickly looked around and noticed that the whole river bank was awash with a thick field of beautiful lady ferns. I grabbed a handful of fronds in one hand, and held Andrea's shoulder firmly with the other. I looked at her seriously, and, firmly and quickly, gave a short speech.

"Look!" I said.

"This will do the job. This is the most powerful pain medicine in the world. It is called 'swizzlebush.' I learned about it from an old Indian, Chief Tom. It is usually too powerful to use on children, but it's all I have, so we'll have to use it, but we'll only do it for five seconds. O.K?

"O.K.," she said.

She grimaced all the while, tears streaming down; I quickly plunged the ferns into the river, getting them sopping wet, and then gently but firmly held them on her knee. I am not quite certain what I expected, but I surely got more than I had bargained for. As I slowly counted out the seconds, the child's face went from pain to what I can only describe as profound surprise, and, by the time I got to five, and ceremoniously jerked away the leaves, she was grinning from ear to ear.

I was dumfounded.

"How does it feel," I asked.

"Fine," she said, still grinning.

And she stood up and, only somewhat gingerly, gamboled off.

As you might imagine, swizzlebush has become somewhat of a family tradition, and has soothed many a bruised elbow and banged shin since that day. On more than one occasion in the dead of winter we have bemoaned the fact that we had none available for such injuries, for sore throats, for headaches.

What happened that day with me and Andrea? Certainly the ferns didn't have much to do with the situation! The cold water may have played a part. Perhaps the knee "didn't *really* hurt," perhaps Andrea only thought it did. Well, it *was* scraped and bleeding, and I *did* see her fall. It sure would have hurt me.

Injury occurs out there on the knee, but "pain" occurs not at the knee but in the brain. And pain is a complex neurological process under equally complex neurological control. Recent research in biochemistry and medicine has shown that the "endorphins," small, rather simple chemicals produced in the brain (which, per-chance, have a structure very similar to opium, which is why opium is an analgesic) are intimately involved in the control of per-ception of pain. One researcher, Dr. Jon Levine of the University of California, has shown in an extraordinary experiment that naloxone, an opiate antagonist—a substance which blocks and in-hibits the action of opiates like morphine or endorphins—also blocks and inhibits "placebo analgesia." Placebos can, somehow, induce the production of endorphins, endogenous opiates. There *is* such a thing as placebo analgesia, it is a very powerful force in medicine and life, and, I am convinced, that day on the Magon-tehon, with a convincing speech and my pathetic handful of "swizzlebush," I triggered Andrea's pain control mechanism. I was very pleased, and very impressed. She was astonished that it felt so much better so quickly—I saw it in her eyes—and so was I!

The key to the event was that Andrea *believed* what I told her. And, as we both saw very clearly, she was justified in her belief.

Her belief was not a consequence of her knowledge, rather of our relationship.

Do I in some sense recommend the use of placebos, of "inert drugs?" I certainly do! Used carefully, judiciously, and forcefully, they can be very effective, very inexpensive, and, most of the time, have no unwanted "side effects." Physicians often argue that it is unethical to use placebos because they have to lie in using them. But it isn't really so. Of course, when I talked to Andrea, I lied. But if I had had my first aid kit, I probably would have told her that the mercurochrome and band aid would make it all better, and that would have been no less a lie. No medicine is ever always effective, or as effective as we might wish—we are, after all, mortal. Placebos aren't always effective; experimental evidence indicates that they are, on the average, effective about 30 or 40 percent of the time, although there are cases on record of much better results (90% of some groups of ulcer patients have been healed with inert pills).

All of that aside, "swizzlebush" has taken its place in our official family pharmacopoeia, at least as effective as mercurochrome smile faces. Keep alert for an equivalent for your family.

## May apples and Cohosh.

*Podophyllum peltatum*

*Caulophyllum thalictroides*

May apples make me lazy. I'm not sure why, but when I see a thick thriving colony of the rich green umbrella plants, I often take the opportunity to sit down, relax, and just daydream. I really don't know what it is about them—perhaps the slowly undulating leaves are hypnotic, a smooth rolling green sea. In the unseen depths, below a leafy surface, the creamy white flowers or, later in the fall, the little "wild lemons" slowly bob and wave beneath a sea without storms or tidal waves or ships. The may apple, *Podophyllum peltatum,* is an important and useful medicinal plant. Long in use by native Americans—by the Iroquois, Fox, Delaware, Cherokee and many others—as a laxative or cathartic, the plant was adopted for these purposes by Euro-Americans early in colonial times. In more recent years, podophyllin, a resin derived from the root has become the drug of choice for topical treatment for "condyloma acuminata," the twenty four dollar name for venereal warts. The may apple has been an official drug in the USP from 1820 until the present day. Several hundred tons of the root are collected every year for both domestic and international markets. As a laxative, may apple root is quite dangerous as only a very small dose can be intensely poisonous. As a tranquilizer, however, a field of may apples swaying before you in the summer heat is unsurpassed.

The blue cohosh, *Caulophyllum thalictroides,* is in the same family as the may apple, but had quite different uses. Cohosh (an Algonquian name) was widely used by native Americans to regulate menstruation and to facilitate childbirth. Fox women used a boiled root tea to contol profuse menstruation as did Menominee and Potawatomi women. The Ojibwa felt that the root relieved the cramps which sometimes accompany menstruation. The Potawatomi, the Cherokee and a number of other groups used cohosh to ease childbirth; for this reason, the plant was widely known as

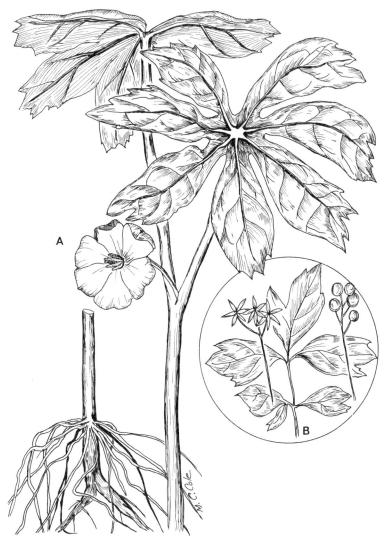

(A) *MAY APPLE*: Podophyllum peltatum. *Two large umbrella-like leaves of May apple shade a single six to nine-petalled white flower. The mature fruit is an edible yellow berry. The twelve to eighteen-inch, showy plants frequently form colonies in clearings, pastures and rich woods.*
(B) *BLUE COHOSH*: Caulophyllum thalictroides. *The small, unusual, greenish-brown, six-pointed flowers rise in stalked clusters above the two to five-lobed leaflets. At maturity, the pods burst to reveal two fleshy blue seeds in this one to three-foot tall plant of the rich woods.*

"papoose root." The root was included in the USP from 1882 until 1905 as a menstrual regulator.

The plant had other uses for native Americans that seem not to have been taken up by whites. The Omaha and Iroquois used a root tea to reduce fevers; the Omaha considered the plant to be extremely effective for this purpose. The Chippewa used the root to treat stomach cramps and indigestion, and the Cherokee used the root for rheumatism.

These two lovely members of a rather unlovely family, the barberries, are examples of the differing fates of native American medicinal plants. One has fallen utterly by the wayside, forgotten, and the other has become the object of vast industrial exploitation. With either of them, however, we can make a personal connection with the indigenous traditions of care and human concern which we call healing.

*MILKWEED:* Asclepias tuberosa. *Monarch butterflies live in close association with these one to two-foot tall milkweeds. The colorful, orange-red summer flowers are borne in terminal clusters. Lance-shaped pods are conspicuous fall fruits of these plants of dry soils and open places.*

## Milkweeds, Monarchs, and Centaurs

*Asclepias tuberosa*

*Asclepias speciosa*

Native Americans used at least seven species of milkweeds medicinally in a variety of ways. The Paiutes and Shoshones used the milky sap, or latex, topically to cure ringworm, and as a dressing on wounds or bruises to prevent infection and to promote healing. The Menominee and Omaha used the root, prepared in several different ways, for the same purposes. The Tewa and Hopi of the Southwest as well as the Chippewa, probably invoking principles of sympathetic magic, used the plant in several formulations to promote the production of milk in new mothers. The Paiute relieved headaches by washing the sufferer's head with the tea made by boiling the root. The Fox drank the root tea as a vermifuge and as an emetic and cathartic purge. A number of groups used the root—pounded, dried, or boiled—to relieve coughs, chest pains, or pleurisy.

Native American enthusiasm for the milkweeds was widely shared by Euro-Americans from the earliest times until the turn of the twentieth century. One species or another was listed in the USP from the first edition in 1820 until at least 1905. It was widely recommended as a purge (very popular in those days). One species, *Asclepias tuberosa*, was so widely used for chest colds, cough, and the like, that, to this day, one of its common names is "pleurisy root."

As a child, I learned in no uncertain terms that milkweed was poisonous. It was one of those things which, at the age of seven, I was sure that "everyone knew." In fact, "everyone" was right. Varying in intensity from species to species, the members of the milkweed family produce a range of poisonous substances known as "cardiac glycosides." Why do plants produce poisons? Why, after all, do plants produce substances that have medicinal value to humans? The answer to these difficult questions has only recently become more clear with the emergence in biology of the ecological study of plant and animal communities. Since the case of milkweeds has been intensively studied, particularly by Biologist Lincoln Brower of Amherst College, I will use it as a prime example, recognizing that it is not unique in principle, but only in detail. But what fascinating detail!

Essentially, some plants, and other living things low on the food chain like mussels, clams, and certain algae and mushrooms, have evolved the capacity to produce noxious distasteful toxins as a defense against those animals higher in the food chain which would feed on them. If, among the plants in some species, certain individuals produce, by chance, certain foul tasting or toxic substances, and, subsequently, they are less likely to be eaten by passing herbivores, they will be more likely to reproduce than will neighboring plants. As a consequence, the next generation of plants will contain a larger percentage of toxic individuals. In outline, this is a straightforward case of what Darwin called natural selection. Both rotenone (derived from several species in the pea family) and nicotine (derived, of course, from tobacco) are well known naturally occurring insecticides which are extracted from plants and used commercially in agriculture. In the United States alone, over 500 tons of nicotine are used in this way each year.

Some plants, rather than producing insecticides, produce herbicides—substances toxic to other plants. This gives them room to grow by inhibiting the growth of nearby plants. Anyone who has ever tried to plant grass under a black walnut tree has come up against this problem.

This however, is not the end of the problem, only the beginning. In a number of cases, certain animal species have been able to break through these defensive maneuvers, and have developed the ability to both tolerate and exploit the toxins which initially defeated them. Monarch butterflies are such a case. Monarchs lay their eggs on the leaves of milkweeds. The fat green striped larvae eat milkweed leaves almost exclusively. In so doing, they absorb varying quantities of the toxic glycosides produced by the plants. This gives these butterflies two decided advantages over all the other insects with which they must compete. First, it provides them with an exclusive source of food. Second, it makes *them* in turn poisonous to their predators, chiefly birds.

Depending on which species of milkweed the larvae have fed, the adults will contain more or less toxin. Biologist Brower, through an ingenious series of experiments, has shown that blue jays seem to enjoy nothing more than to feast on nontoxic monarchs. They catch the butterflies by the wings, fly to a branch, and proceed to pull off the wings and feet, then eat the abdomen and thorax. The first time a jay is presented with a toxic monarch, he will do the same thing, and a moment or two later (shades of the Fox Indians) the bird will vomit. Subsequently, most such birds will just avoid monarchs completely.

But again, the story is yet more complicated. Monarchs store different kinds, and different concentrations, of glycosides in different parts of their bodies. Simplifying somewhat, it seems as if the toxins in the wings are more bitter, while the ones in the abdomen are more emetic. This enhances the learning process of the birds, and, as they taste the wings first, provides them with a stronger reminder of what is to come if they finish their meal. And it is apparently for this reason that so many butterflies can be found, living and breeding, with scars on their wings—the only reminder of an earlier brush with an avian predator.

But even this is not the end of our chain. For while the monarchs are protected from the jays by their chemical defense, just as the butterflies have broken the defense of the milkweeds, some other birds have broken the defense of the butterflies. In another extraordinary adaption, the monarchs have developed the capacity to migrate several thousand miles from their summer feeding and breeding grounds in the northern United States to the mountains of northern Mexico where they spend the winters. Since the monarchs who migrate one year are two or three generations removed from the previous group of migrants, this is a particularly complex process.

The monarchs spend the winter in several densely packed colonies in Mexico. A half dozen sites have been discovered, averaging about two acres in size, several of which were occupied by over 100 *million* butterflies! Here the birds are not as easily deterred as are the blue jays. Not all milkweeds produce cardiac glycosides and as many as twenty five or thirty percent of monarchs contain only negligible quantities of these toxins. Twenty five percent of a hundred million butterflies in an area the size of two suburban yards is a *lot* of bird food. And the orioles and grosbeaks of northern Mexico have apparently learned how to fly into the packed butterflies (tree branches bending over under their weight), taste the wings, and if they are acceptable, eat them, and if not, let them go. The birds eat an average of 10,000 to 12,000 butterflies per day in each of the colonies studied. The incredibly dense packing of the butterflies is, apparently, *their* response to this predation—an individual maximizes his own chances for survival by hiding himself in the crowd. Only about one or two percent will be eaten over the winter.

Action and reaction, offense and defense, connection and interaction are all part of an extraordinary set of ecological relationships, all built on a foundation of the attempt of a modest North American plant to defend itself against the casual browsing of deer, beaver, and worms.

As the orioles and grosbeaks learned to avoid the toxin, the Fox Indians and Colonial Americans learned to use it, to purge themselves when their medical wisdom told them they should. There are probably between 350,000 and 500,000 species of plants on Earth—no one is quite sure. Each of them produces a number of chemical substances, each for its own purposes of growth, reproduction, offense, defense. That some of these chemicals affect humans in one way or another, for better or worse, is hardly surprising. The *endorphins*, substances produced in the human brain and elsewhere which have a structure and physiological action very similar to that of opium, where discovered in 1975. Whatever opium may do for poppies (I haven't the faintest idea), it is not produced so humans can have a massive world-wide drug trade! Rather, by some odd (or perhaps not so odd) chance, these plants produce a substance which happens to have a massive neurological consequence for vertebrates.

Chiron the Centaur was the son of Kronos (the sun) and Philyra; skilled in hunting, music and medicine, he is best remembered as the teacher of Asklepios, the first physician. The milkweeds, named after the great doctor, are our foremost link to his teacher. Half man, half horse, Chiron cannot help but remind us that the boundaries we throw up around nature—plant, animal, beast, human, male, female—are but artificial fences, and that in order to know our world we must not only know the differences between things, but also the connections between them. As you walk through the fields in the fall, and see the silky parachutes of the milkweed seeds trying to break the bonds of their craggy pods, liberate a few—blow them to the winds. The butterflies will, at that moment, be arriving in their Mexican wintering grounds. But they will return in May or June, and you will be able to find the fat striped larvae, and the glorious golden monarchs, perhaps on a milkweed you helped to grow. And you will count yourself part of an extraordinary adaptive network along with Chiron and Asklepios, milkweeds, butterflies, orioles and jays. Good company, and good medicine.

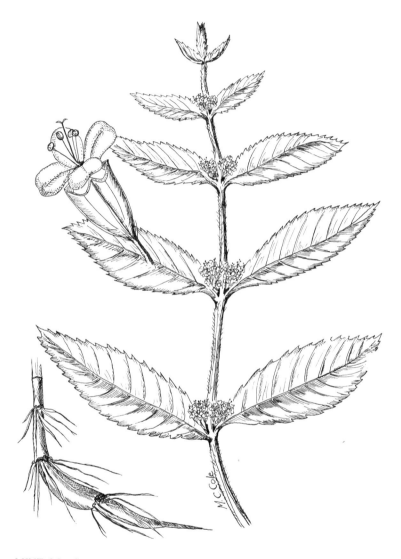

*MINT: Mentha arvensis. The downy or hairless leaves of this square stemmed mint are strong in both flavor and odor. Numerous violet-blue flowers are borne in the axils of the oppositely arranged leaves. The plant, from two to four feet tall, grows on dry ground, in thickets and prairies.*

### Mint, Persephone's legacy.

*Mentha arvensis*

Native Americans found many uses for the one indigenous American species of mint, *Metha arvensis*. A number of groups boiled the leaves in water, then drank the liquid for headaches. Other groups made a warm compress with this liquid and applied it to the forehead for the same purpose. Three Great Basin tribes, the Paiute, Shoshone, and Washoe, gave mint tea to children for stomach aches, indigestion, or colic. These same groups also used mint tea as an antidiarrheal, while the Cheyenne used it as an antiemetic, to prevent vomiting. Several tribes used mint to relieve the congestion and discomfort of colds; the Paiute used the crushed leaves as an inhalant, while the Carrier and Thompson Indians of Western Canada drank mint tea for colds. The Thompson Indians also placed mint leaves in their steam baths to relieve aching muscles and rheumatic joints.

Contemporary biomedicine uses mint in two ways. First, it is, of course, a common flavoring agent in many medicines. Second menthol, which is derived from peppermint oil, is a useful antiprurient, that is, an agent to stop itching. When applied to the skin, menthol has a mild anesthetic property to nerves which perceive pain, and a mild stimulating property to nerves which perceive cold, hence the cooling quality of mint.

There are a dozen European and Asian species of mint which have been naturalized in North America—many of them have cross-bred to produce a profusion of strains. They all contain more or less the same active principles though in different proportions.

Mint was an important herb in the humoral medicine of old Europe. Considered to be "hot and dry," it was recommended for "phlegmatic" illnesses, that is, cold, damp ones. Its hot and dry nature may have been a consequence, in part, of its origin. Thus, Aristotle's famous student Theophrastus tells us that Hades, the god of the (hot, dry?) underworld, emerged one day into the air whereupon he attempted to ravage the nymph Minthe. Persephone, Hades' aggrieved spouse, stumbled upon the scene, and, in an act of righteous vigor, saved the nymph's honor (and perhaps her own) by turning her into the sweet herb. For a thousand years thereafter, mint was placed around the bodies of the dead, some say, to deter the Evil One who, seeing mint, would recall his ignominy, and retreat; other more prosaic thinkers have suggested the custom was more employed to mask the smells of death. These interpretations do not seem to me mutually exclusive.

There are two reasonable contemporary uses of mint. First, a crumbled fresh leaf rubbed on a mosquito bite will stop the itching. Second, a hot mint tea, best made by pouring boiling water over a sprig of bruised fresh leaves, is a soothing drink for one with a stuffy head cold or headache.

Mint is, perhaps, *too* easily grown. The problem is not to grow it, but to prevent it from overrunning the entire garden (and the lawn, and the neighbor's lawn ...). The plants send out runners just at the surface of the soil, sometimes forming a thick mat. If, in digging the herb out of a patch of ground you neglect to remove a tiny piece of root, it will sprout and spread all over again (shades of the Sorcerer's Apprentice). Fortunately, the roots spread at the surface, and are easily contained by surrounding the plants with aluminum lawn edging, or closely spaced bricks. Once planted, either from roots or from seeds easily obtained at your garden supply store, the perennial herb requires no particular care. Pinching off the tiny blue flowers will encourage a bushier growth, but is not really necessary.

As is often the case with herbs once having wide medicinal use, this one has taken its place in the culinary arts. Add a dozen or more fresh leaves to a lettuce salad (or to iced tea) for a pleasing color and stimulating taste. Home made mint jelly far surpasses the commercial variety as an accompaniment to lamb or pork.

There is a more direct approach to this association of mint and meat which is simply superb. Select a leg of lamb suited to the size of your gathering. Bone it, and, with a large knife, cut the leg so it lies flat, about an inch to an inch and a half thick. For a six pound roast, mix together a quarter cup of olive oil, ten finely chopped mint leaves, a tablespoon of rosemary, two finely chopped garlic cloves, and salt and pepper to taste. Rub this mixture on the inside of the boned leg. Then, with butcher cord, roll the roast up like a jelly-roll with the fat side out. Roast in a 375° oven for about 30 minutes per pound, until a meat thermometer registers about 175°. Serve with roast potatoes and peas, cooked with tarragon.

The same filling may be used in boned pork loin (cook to 170° on the meat thermometer). This is *particularly* good when sliced cold the next day. Whenever I cook this, I confess, I (somewhat furtively) thank Persephone, and (more publicly) praise the virtue of unsullied nymphs.

*AMERICAN MISTLETOE:* Phoradendron flavenscens. *American Mistletoe is a parasitic shrub which grows on the trunks and branches of deciduous trees. It is shown on*Acacaia amanta, *a western legume. It has smooth, jointed twigs and leathery, green leaves. The oblong, rounded leaves are arranged opposite one another. The white berries grow on short stalks.*

## Mistletoe, the meaningful medicine.

*Arceuthobium campylopodum*

*Phoradendron flavenscens*

This will be the most complicated chapter in this book. I am going to develop an argument which may seem somewhat far-fetched, but I am doing it for a reason. Among native Americans, the word "medicine" had a larger meaning than we usually attach to the word. By medicine, most native Americans meant some thing, a plant, a mineral, a song, a painting, that somehow influenced the world, or people, or the relationship between people and the world. Now, if you think about it, that is sort of what *we* mean by the word, but we usually don't think of it that way. We tend to think of it in "categorical" rather than "functional" terms. Medicine is the stuff we get from the "drug aisle" at the grocery store, or with a prescription from the doctor. But if we think of what medicine *does* rather than what it *is*, the word seems to get bigger. The broader definition is probably more accurate, and certainly more useful if we want to understand human behavior.

"This is a great shirt. I've had it for seven years, it's almost worn out; it's so comfortable, that when I put it on, I just relax—the kids' hollering doesn't bother me—and, well, I just feel better with this shirt on." That's medicine, something that changes me, changes the way I feel, changes my relationships with the people around me, changes the quality of my life and, for all intents and purposes, changes the world. You might want to quibble by telling me that my old shirt only changes *my* world, not *the* world, but I guess I would have to come back by saying that I have a real hard time telling the difference.

Our Western medicine usually looks very different than American Indian medicine. Sometimes it is not all that different: we take our aspirin in pills, and they take it in pussy willow tea (see our chapter on pussy willows). But it usually *looks* different. And that is why mistletoe is so helpful because it is one case where our medicine looks a lot like theirs.

Why is it that at Christmas we hang up little sprigs of mistletoe in doorways? When I ask this question, people tend to look puzzled, and say, "Well, I guess people have always done it." This is the equivalent to the answer to a thousand questions asked by hundreds of anthropologists, in hundreds of languages: "It's our custom." But why do we have *this* custom rather than any number of other ones I might imagine (standing around the nut bowl singing old German folk songs; decorating the windows with oak leaves)? We don't do those things; instead, modern Americans suspend sprigs of *Phoradendron flavescens* or *Arceuthobium campylopodum* in their homes and offices, and there, in a remarkable exception to normal standards of decorum, they kiss and hug friend and stranger alike.

The reasons that we do this are, you will see, complex; and the reasons are like the ones that are behind a good deal of the rather broader ideas of medicine held by most native Americans. To begin, we have to learn something about the plant.

The most striking natural quality of mistletoe is that it is a parasitic plant. It grows not in the ground, but as a parasite on trees. It has no roots, but a special organ known to botanists as a "haustorium" by which it attaches itself to a host from which it obtains nutrients and water.

While these elements of the nature of the plant have simply been incorporated into the botanist's definition of the family Loranthaceae, they have made it more difficult for ordinary people to pigeonhole the plant in their simpler but otherwise comprehensive and reasonable folk classifications of nature. The plant seems to defy classification as it sits on the edge of a number of different categories and not squarely in any of them. In a representative instance, 10th century Arabian scholars decided that parasitic plants had animal souls, feeding as might worms on the juices of their hosts; to these observers, the plant bridged that fundamental division between plant and animal.

Anthropologists have noticed that in many cultures such awkward natural species have been selected to play special and often decisive roles in ritual and myth. We find that these "anomalous" (that is, "nameless," or "category-less") creatures are often used in ritual to bridge gaps between symbolic categories just as they seem to bridge gaps in nature. Their gap-bridging quality leads us to refer to them as "mediators"; because they fall between standard categories, they are sometimes said to be "interstructural."

Consider a few examples from native North America. In its parasitism, the mistletoe shares important characteristics with the raven and coyote, both of which (rightly or wrongly) have the reputation of being carrion-eating scavengers. These animals are models for two common characters in native American mythology. Among many Eskimo and Northwest Coast groups like the Tsimshian and Kwakiutl, Raven is the trickster who travels around causing terrible trouble as he creates the world as we know it. Coyote plays a similar mythological role for many native peoples of the Plains and Southwest. Thirty years ago, the famous French anthropologist Claude Levi-Strauss described the essential anomaly of Coyote and Raven when he wrote that "carrion-eating animals are like beasts of prey (they eat animal food), but they are also like food-plant producers (they do not kill what they eat)." Similarly, mistletoe is like a plant (it has leaves and berries), but it is also like a herbivorous animal (it lives on plants).

One can go a bit farther with this by asking what carrion is. It is not simply meat from a dead animal; it is meat which is partially rotten, partially transformed back into the soil—that is, it is a substance which bridges the gap between what we might think of as life and the dust from which we came and to which we will return: not still meat, not yet dust.

It is frequently the eating habits of animals which lead people to see them "betwixt and between" the standard categories. At first glance, for instance, the rabbit would seem to be the definitive herbivore. Consider, however, the following information from the *Encyclopedia Britannica*. The rabbit regularly produces two kinds of fecal pellets, "dry and hard, and soft and moist. The latter kind, which appear to contain vitamins and metabolic products, are eaten, often directly from the anus. The nutritional effect of this practice has been compared to that of rumination in cows." This may be the basis for the otherwise curious injunction from Leviticus, "The hare, because it chews the cud but has not a parted foot; you shall regard it as unclean" (11:5-6). It may also account for the fact that the Cherokee trickster is not a coyote or a raven, but a giant rabbit.

Some of these anomalous creatures are very widely recognized as having special qualities. Indeed, the raven has been a strong symbolic presence for Europeans as well as for native Americans. One can read Genesis 8:6-7 in this way: "After forty days Noah released a raven which flew back and forth drying the water off the earth." Shakespeare, in one notable passage in his worst play, linked the raven and mistletoe when he had a character describe a "barren detested vale" as populated only by "trees ... o'ercome with moss and baleful mistletoe, ... owl ... raven ... fiends ... toads (and) urchins (that is, hedgehogs)," a veritable zoo of interstructural creatures (Tamora, Queen of the Goths, in *Titus Andronicus* II:3:93-104). And ravens populate many of Grimm's fairy tales and other European folk literature.

Mistletoe, even more than ravens, is a very special species, anomalous in dimensions beyond its parasitism. Consider its mode of propagation. Although mistletoe seed can be "sown" directly, it seems likely that most propagation occurs through the intervention of birds which eat the whitish berries and then leave their droppings on nearby tree branches. Several species of birds, especially the European mistletoe thrush, *Turdus viscivorus*, seem to prefer mistletoe berries to any other food. Another bird, the mistletoe flowerpecker, *Dicaeum celebicum*, also lives in a symbiosis with certain tropical American mistletoe species. Several observers agree that this bird has certain difficulties voiding the rather large seed of its favored food. One authority tells us that, when defecating, the bird suddenly squats and simultaneously shifts its position with astonishing agility along the twig while its body rocks to and fro, thus covering a distance of 8 to 10 inches. In other words, the bird actually pastes the seeds to the branch.

Summarizing the knowledge of the ancient world on the topic, Pliny tells us, refering to the European species, *Viscus album*,

> When mistletoe seed is sown it never sprouts at all, and only when passsed in the excrement of birds, particularly the pigeon and the thrush: its nature is such that it will not shoot unless it has been ripened in the stomach of birds (XVI:42).

Our own name for the plant seems to derive from this aspect of it: the German "Mistel" is derived from "Mist," meaning manure.

This intimate relationship with birds provides additional anomaly for mistletoe since birds are *themselves* in several ways anomalous. Recalling Plato's mocking definition of humans as "featherless bipeds," we recognize that birds are by half of their nature metaphorically human: bipedal, familial, vocal, cultured (especially in their construction activities). Yet by another half of their nature, they are distinctly animal: egg-laying, feathered, winged. These two-legged creatures can walk about like people, yet momentarily fly off into the heavens. They decisively mediate human life and animal life, culture and nature, earth and heaven, and easily cross broad cosmological gaps.

And so, mistletoe doubly mediates natural realms: it is a plant whose seed must be consumed by the mediating bird, and voided as excrement—something which was once food, but is now its antithesis. That which in the normal course would decay (as might carrion) and become again earth, here shows life, sprouts, and grows, not in the fertile earth, but in the branches of a living tree, producing a strange creature, a herbivorous, rootless plant.

This odd plant plays a role in many interesting human traditions. In twelve thick volumes, James Frazier's *Golden Bough* sorted out (and jumbled up again) the many myths and traditions of the King of the Wood in the sacred grove of Diana, goddess of the moon and of hunting. The King was killed in mortal combat every year by the new, young claimant to the throne after he had plucked from the sacred tree a golden bough, which Frazier identified as mistletoe. In another tradition, according to Pliny, Celtic priests, the Druids, had a central role for mistletoe in their monthly rites for the moon, "sacrificing a bough of the plant before dispatching two white bulls, this on the sixth day of the moon because it is then rising in strength and not one half its full size" (XVI:45), neither this nor that. In both these traditions, the mistletoe, all-purpose mediator, sanctions a trans-action, an action across a boundary, passing on power from one king to the next, insuring the movement from the new moon to the full.

The most interesting story of the mistletoe is the myth of Loki and Balder from Snorri Sturulson's great *Prose Edda*, written in Iceland in the 13th century. The *Edda*, a textbook for apprentice poets, summarized and organized a mass of mythic and legendary

*DWARF MISTLETOE:* Arceuthobium campylopodum. *These dwarf plants grow in clusters on the branches of junipers and pines: it is shown here on the lodgepole pine,* Pinus contorta. *The olive-colored branches have tiny scale-like leaves, but conspicuous, egg-shaped fruits. The branching stems reach a length of about three inches.*

material, the core of Teutonic oral tradition. Odin himself tells Gylfi, the King of Sweden, the tale of Balder's death at Loki's hand. Balder the good, the most beloved of the gods, has a series of dreams foretelling his death. His mother, Frigga, wife of Odin, decides to prevent this, and extracts promises from all things—fire, water, iron, metal, stones, earth, trees, sicknesses, beasts, birds, venom, serpents—that they will never harm Balder. The gods make sport of Balder's new immunity, throwing stones, missiles, arrows at him, but none hurt him, all swerve aside.

Loki is the trickster. He is the son, more or less, of a giant; he is able to change his form, change his sex. After a dalliance with the great stallion Svadilfari, Loki gives birth to Sleipnir, an eight-legged horse, ultimately Odin's own. Loki, following the trickster's urge to confuse (to fuse together), disguises himself as a woman and asks Frigga whether all things have taken the oath not to harm Balder. She says they have, but, "there grows a tree-sprout alone westward of Valhall: it is called Mistletoe; I thought it too insignificant to ask the oath of." Loki gathers the parasitic herb, makes a slender dart and approaches Balder's blind brother Hoder, who is not pelting Balder. Loki convinces Hoder to do his brother the honor of playing; Hoder throws the dart guided by Loki. Balder, pierced through, falls dead. One of the primary, categorical, universal boundaries has been breached: the immortal gods have felt the sting of human death. Loki subverts a vast attempt to ransom Balder from the underworld. The other gods catch him. One of Loki's sons is turned into a wolf which tears asunder another son, whose entrails are used to bind Loki to a rock in a cave. A serpent drips venom in his face; his wife catches the drips in a bowl. When she goes to empty the bowl, the venom hits the trickster who twists in pain with such force as to cause the earth to tremble; these are earthquakes.

The suggestion of Prometheus is strong; both Prometheus and Loki narrowed the difference between men and gods and suffered horribly for it. Prometheus made men more like gods with the gift of fire; Loki made the gods more like mortal men, his instrument the anomalous mistletoe.

Back in North America, we find the mistletoe was used medicinally by a number of different tribes. The uses were various—analgesics, antidiarrheals, stomach remedies, panaceas—but one particular set of customs stands out. A Papago woman with menstrual cramps will lie on a bed of warmed mistletoe plants. The Zuni use the mistletoe along with the juniper on which it grows to make a tea which is drunk to ease the pains and facilitate the process of childbirth. Several other groups use various mistletoe formulations to arrest bleeding after childbirth. Some investigators have suggested that mistletoe may have "oxytocic properties" ("oxytocin" is a hormone that stimulates contractions in the muscles of the uterus). And well it may. But I prefer to see its use sanctioned here for the same reason that it is appropriate for the Druids at monthly ceremonials: this interstructural plant effectively marks the zone of rebirth, or in these cases, birth itself.

In all the cases we have considered, it is this way. The mistletoe marks the spaces in between; it marks the edge, the end of the old and the start of the new. It is, thereby, a perfectly appropriate symbol for the solstice, when we lose the old year, and gain the new. With mistletoe we can be certain that the gap will be bridged, that the sun will sink no lower on the horizon, and will come back again bringing new life in the springs. Hanging up mistletoe is a New Year custom, not a Christmas custom. Indeed, *Christmas* is a New Year custom! We mark our own solstice ceremony with a whole constellation of celebration: with Christmas, when the human god is born signaling a new age of salavation; with Hanukkah, celebrating the rededication of the Second Temple in Jerusalem; and with ribald singing, dancing, funny hats, Bacchanalianism and masquerade, all common marks of festival associated with rebirth or renewal (as at wedding celebrations). In this case, we are celebrating a rite of passage, a "birthday" of a sort, for the earth itself.

And so, the mistletoe seems an appropriate symbol for the solstice. But we don't merely hang it up, we *kiss* people under it! What's the kissing about? A kiss is a sign of intimacy, a gesture shared by lovers or kinsmen. No one needs mistletoe to kiss his spouse or child. Mistletoe—millions of dollars worth annually—is mostly hung up in business offices, where it marks the zone for kissing strangers. And we see it continues to exert its strong implicit communication: Just as, in the dimension of time, the old year confronts, contacts, the new, in the dimension of social class, bosses kiss their secretaries.

And so at the new year, we find ourselves standing under the parasitic herb, propagated in the dung of birds, kissing strangers, marking time, following a logic we share with Icelandic poets, Celtic priests, Papago and Cherokee Indians, and (can it be?) Tamora, Queen of the Goths, in good company, bending nature to our needs and acting out in human symbolic terms an annual renewal of the earth we live on.

*       *       *

Well, I told you it would seem a bit far-fetched. But if you don't understand how a plant can have meaning, and how that meaning can influence the world as people live in it, you will necessarily misunderstand the medicine of native American peoples. This is not to say that their medicines do not have real physiological properties; most assuredly they do! But medicine never has *only* physiological properties. It also always has *meaningful* properties. Sometimes, perhaps most of the time, it is as hard to understand the meaningful properties as it is to understand the physiological ones. And just because we don't know exactly what the meaning is doesn't mean that there isn't one.

Mistletoe, like my old shirt, is good medicine. You hang it up in doorways to be certain that Spring will come. If you have to purchase your mistletoe, be sure to discard the little white plastic berries that are so often attached to it. One hates even to think of their significance.

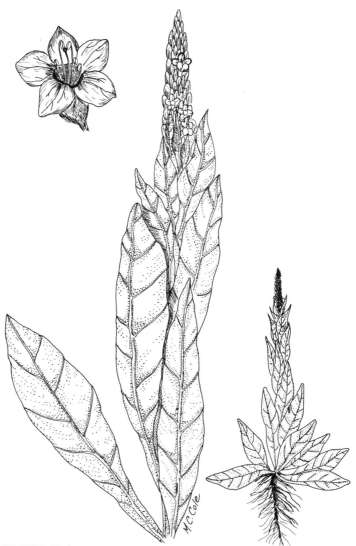

*MULLEIN:* Verbascum thapsus. *Common mullein, three to six feet tall, is easily recognized by its soft, hairy, oblong leaves and terminal spike of yellow flowers. The large, grayish-green basal leaves grow on short stalks. Mullein is found in waste places, fields and roadsides.*

## Mullein, a plant "on the road."

*Verbascum thapsus*

Mullein, *Verbascum thapsus*, is a plant native to Europe and Asia. It is named after the Mediterranean Island of Thapsos where, apparently, it was very common in classical times. It was introduced early into the new world where it was quickly taken up by native Americans as a useful medicine. It is a classic example of the affinity which introduced plants have for disturbed ground and waste places; if we were to rename the species and follow classical precedent by naming it after the place we find it, it would surely be called *Verbascum interstaticus*, for the plant seems to be most at home "on the road."

The ancient Romans, medieval Europeans, native Americans, and 19th century American physicians all show remarkable agreement on the proper uses of this plant, primarily as a treatment for chest and lung diseases, and for rheumatic conditions.

The Mohegan, Delaware, Cherokee and Creek drank teas of the root or leaves for coughs. The Navajo smoked the leaves for coughs, and the Mohegan smoked them for asthma and sore throat as did the Penobscot, Potawatomi, and Iroquois. Pliny tells us that the Romans used the leaf tea for tonsillitis. In the last century, the plant was commonly smoked by Euro-Americans for coughs, and had a brief vogue as a treatment for tuberculosis.

Similarly, the plant had a widespread reputation as an effective treatment for rheumatic joints and physical injuries. The Delaware used the heated leaves as a poultice for rheumatism, while country people in South Carolina boil mullein with pine branches to make a liniment for the same condition. Pliny recommended a similar concoction for dislocated joints, abscesses and wounds, as did Gerard, the 16th century herbalist, and many 19th century American physicians.

The plant had other less widespread uses as well. The Hopi mixed it with some other herbs, then smoked it to stop convulsions. The Nanticoke bound the leaves to the neck, forehead and wrists for fever. The Iroquois used the leaf tea for rashes, especially on babies; they also put the leaves in their shoes for softness and to treat smelly feet.

Mullein was listed in the NF from 1888 until 1936 and, as has been noted, was used for coughs and rashes. Mullein tea is a mildly stimulating drink, probably of some value for stuffed heads and mild coughs. Certainly, it is to be recommended as a plaster for blisters developed while hiking—the soft furry leaves will cushion the tender spot, and may encourage healing as well.

## Oaks, red and white.

*Quercus alba*

*Quercus rubra*

The oaks, rich sources of astringent tannins, saw wide native American use for a variety of purposes. At least a dozen species were used, equally divided between the white oaks (leaves with rounded lobes) and red oaks (leaves with pointed lobes). Almost all of the uses of the oaks can be accounted for in terms of the tannins they contain which dry up and heal sores and excess mucous secretions, accounting for the oaks' effectiveness in treating cuts, sores, coughs, diarrhea and so on.

The Ojibwa used both the white oak, *Quercus alba*, and the red oak, *Q. rubra*, to treat diarrhea. They drank a boiled bark and root bark tea. Other tribes—the Fox, Houma, Potawatomi and Creek—used similar treatments. The Delaware used bark teas of several species of oak for cough and cold remedies, while several tribes from the Northern Plains—the Dakota, Omaha, Pawnee and Winnebago—used oak root bark teas to treat colic in children. The Navajo and Chippewa made similar medicines for adults with stomach aches or cramps. The Delaware, Alabama and Houma used bark teas for sore throats.

Many tribes used oak teas or oak bark dressings on wounds. The Alabama used oak bark tea on sores, while the Chippewa used oak root bark as a dressing for wounds in order to stop bleeding. The Iroquois combined the astringent and symbolic qualities of oak in an interesting cure. When an oak branch had broken and partly grown back, they said, it looked like a navel; therefore, when an infant's navel was not healing properly after birth, one should scrape the bark from the healed oak branch, powder it, and sprinkle it on the sore spot. A double barreled cure!

Several tribes used oak teas to treat rheumatism, as did some country people with whom I spoke about the matter in the early 1970s in the South Carolina Sea Islands.

Oak bark has been used medicinally in Europe for millenia, for

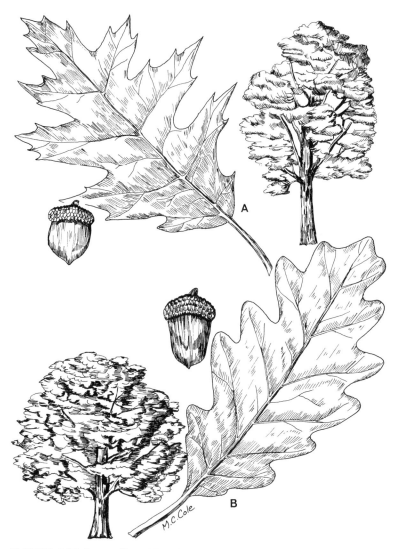

(**A**) *WHITE OAK:* Quercus alba. (**B**) *RED OAK:* Quercus rubra. *Red and white oaks are readily separated by distinctive characteristics. The white oaks* (**A**), *with their rounded leaf lobes, and oblong, sweet acorns, have spreading crowns. In contrast, the red oaks* (**B**), *with their pointed leaf lobes and round, bitter acorns, have a more rounded crown.*

much the same purposes as it was used by native Americans, for diarrheas and for wounds. The inner bark of white oak was listed in the USP from 1820 until 1916, and in the NF from 1916 until 1936 as an astringent and tonic. The first USP noted that to make "Decoctum Quercus," one should add an ounce of white oak bark to two pints of water and boil it down to one pint, then strain.

Although these medicinal uses of oak were important in European history, the religious and ritual significance of oaks certainly eclipsed the medicinal. Oaks were sacred to a whole list of European gods, among them Jehovah, Zeus, Jupiter, Hercules, Demeter, Thor, and a dozen more. The oak was often associated with the sun and celestial fire since all knew it attracted lighting; people protected their homes from lightning by planting oaks nearby—and only a fool would have used oak boards to make a roof. In certain European regions, the oak was so sacred that it was forbidden to cut one down; oaks which *were* cut down were known to scream and moan as they crashed to the ground.

Recently I planted an oak tree in the back yard. I found a small sapling about two feet tall in a nearby woods slated to be the site of a condominium. So I dug it up, took it home, dug a hole, and watered it in. This spring it is growing nicely. It should reach its mature size in the twenty second century. To plant one is to offer up a faith in the future. They tower over us, all seeing—some would say all knowing:

> I robbed the Woods —
> The trusting Woods.
> The unsuspecting Trees
> Brought out their Burs and mosses
> My fantasy to please.
> I scanned their trinkets curious —
> I grasped—I bore away —
> What will the solemn Hemlock —
> What will the Oak tree say?
>
> Emily Dickinson, ca. 1858

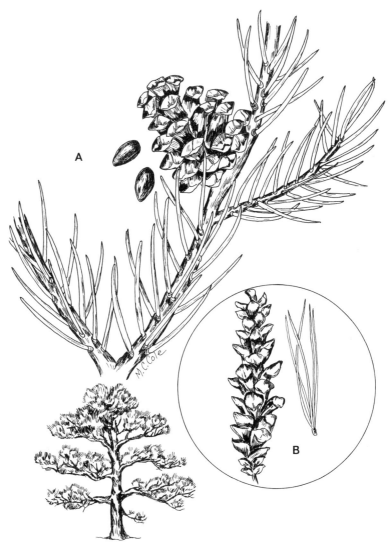

(A) *PINON PINE: Pinus monophylla. Single, one to one-and-a-half-inch needles grow from the branches and stems of the Pinon pine. Edible seeds are produced in the two-inch-long cones. These 20 to 60-foot, rounded-crown trees grow in rocky, dry areas of the Western United States.* (B) *WHITE PINE: Pinus alba. The Eastern White Pine has clusters of five needles, three to five inches long. Cylindrical cones, five to eight inches long, grow on these tall trees (up to 100 feet). They thrive in areas of fertile, well drained, sandy soil.*

## Of pines and turpentines.

*Pinus monophylla*

*Pinus strobus*

When most of us think of "turpentine," our first, and probably only, thought is of "paint thinner." It seems strange to think of turpentine as medicine, but it *is* a medicine, and has been one for thousands of years.

The word turpentine is derived from *terebinthos*, the Greek name for the terebinth tree, *Pistacia terebinthus*, a fairly common tree of the Near East which exudes a resin which was the first "turpentine." This resin, like other such substances as balsam (see our chapter on Balsams), has a distinct antibiotic character, and was used as a plaster for wounds in antiquity. Pliny considered terebinth to be the best of a dozen available resins for cleaning and closing wounds; he also noted that it was excellent for chest complaints when taken internally. The terebinth is classified in the same genus as the mastic tree, *Pistacia lenta*, source of mastic or balm, which was widely used in antiquity and into modern times as a chewing gum ("mastic" means to chew) which would strengthen teeth and gums. The other famous member of this genus is *P. vera*, the pistachio.

By about the 14th or 15th century, the English "turpentine" had begun to refer to the chemically similar oleoresins exuded by pines rather than the terebinth resins. In contemporary usage, "turpentine" is the actual oleoresin or sap obtained from pine trees. This substance, commercially gathered today in northern Florida, Georgia, and the Carolinas, is distilled to produce "oil of turpentine." Oil of turpentine is sometimes treated with sodium hydroxide, and distilled again; this yields "rectified turpentine oil" which has essentially the same properties as oil of turpentine but without the strong odor and taste. When rectified turpentine oil is treated with nitric acid and alcohol, it becomes terpinol or terpin hydrate, which is a stimulant to the mucuous membranes and acts as an expectorant; it is a common ingredient in cough syrups. Oil of turpentine, plain or rectified, has many medicinal uses, particuarly as a local stimulant or "rubefacient"; when rubbed on the skin as a liniment, it enhances the flow of blood, and reduces muscular or joint pain. It is also an antiseptic. Taken internally, either form, like terpin hydrate, acts as an expectorant helping to clear the chest and head of excess mucus and thereby aid breathing. It is also a moderately effective vermifuge. Several varieties of turpentine were official medicines for over a century, and several other pine products (pine oil, pine tar, rosin) were as well; several still are.

Native Americans used various pine products, either the turpentine or various bark or leaf teas, for much the same purposes as did Europeans. The most commonly used species were the singleleaf pinon, *Pinus monophylla*, and the white pine, *P. strobus*, although eight or ten other species were used as well. The most common uses, as in Europe, were on wounds and for chest colds. For example, the Chippewa, Micmac, Delaware, Potawatomi, Menominee and Mohegan all used the white pine in one way or another to treat wounds, sores, boils or abscesses. They usually used the sap as a salve or bound the inner bark of the tree directly on the wound. The Paiute and Shoshone heated the resin of the singleleaf pinon and used it as a dressing on boils or splinters. Moreover, the Paiute mixed the resin with boiling water and drank the liquid for colds. The Delaware boiled a tea of white pine twigs to make a medicine for chest colds while the Montagnais used the white pine resin in much the same way as the Paiute in a tea for colds and coughs.

There were many other uses for the pines as well. In British Columbia, several groups used the sap or leaves of the lodgepole pine, *Pinus contorta*, in liniments for rheumatic conditions. The Bella Coola heated the sap and applied it to sore joints while the Thompson Indians used the sap as the base for a salve for rheumatism. The Potawatomi boiled the cones of the jack pine, *P. banksiana*, to obtain their resin which was then used as an ointment on sores and wounds. The Thompson Indians used the gum of the ponderosa pine, *P. ponderosa*, mixed with grease as a salve for sore and inflamed eyes.

There are dangers associated with the medicinal uses of the various pine products. In large quantities, oil of turpentine can cause vomiting, convulsions, shock and death. If you are tempted to try these substances, be prudent and use the smallest amount which is effective; one or two cubic centimeters of turpentine oil, or about a quarter of a teaspoon, was a standard adult dose in years gone by.

And so turpentine is *not* only a paint thinner, but an old and honored member of the human medical tradition. Not only do the pines provide us with this useful substance, they, of course, provide excellent lumber, and, from several southwestern pinon pines, we get pine nuts, among the most delectable foods ever discovered by humanity. Pliny noted that, for those convalescing from serious illnesses, the air in districts planted with pines was more healthful than a sea-voyage to Egypt; better medical advice—wander through pine forests breathing deeply—would be hard to find.

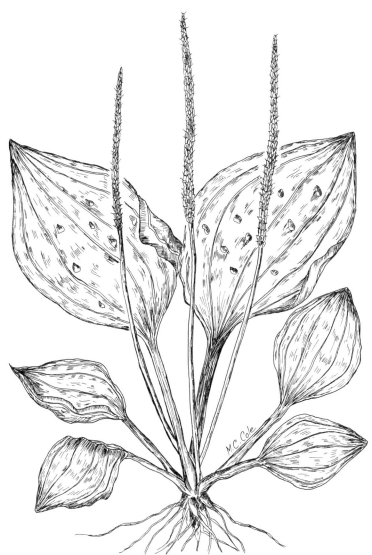

*PLANTAIN:* Plantago major. *Broad, spade-shaped leaves at the base of the plantain encircle one or more tall stalks. Tightly flowered spikes are borne at the ends of the stalks. Plantain, found on roadsides, wet places, and lawns grows five to eighteen inches tall.*

## Plantain, the "white man's footprint."

### *Plantago major*

The common plantain, *Plantago major*, may be the single most readily found medicinal plant in North America, tied for first place, perhaps, with the dandelion. This plant, introduced from Europe, rapidly spread across the continent, taking up residence in fields and on roadsides; it is today a common weed in suburban yards. Some Indian tribes are said to have referred to it as the "white man's footprint" as it seemed to show up everywhere he did. This may or may not be an accurate etymology; the Latin name for the plant, *Plantago*, means, more or less, "footprint" referring to the form of the leaf, and this suggests that "white man's footprint" may be a term of European origin.

The plant has an ancient history as a medicine in Europe. Pliny recommended it for just about everything: as a cautery (to stop bleeding), as an astringent, for diarrhea and catarrh (stuffed head), for toothache, scrofula, stomach illnesses, kidney illnesses, for loss of appetite, for intestinal problems, for the bladder, and on and on. Perhaps its most common use in Europe was as a dressing for cuts and bruises—a recommendation made by Gerard in his *Herbal*, and by poor Costard, the clown herald in Shakespeare's *Love's Labor's Lost*, who, having banged his shin, wanted a bandage of plantain but instead got a lot of badinage.

Native Americans quickly adopted the introduced plant finding it most useful for burns, cuts, and bruises. The Fox and Ojibwa used the leaves on burns, while the Delaware, Ojibwa, Cherokee, and a half dozen other tribes used them on bruises and cuts. The Mohegan used the leaves as a poultice for insect or snake bites.

Several indigenous North American species were used much the same way. The Houma made a salve of grease and heart-shaped plantain, *Plantago cordata*, which they used on cuts, sores, burns and boils. The Menominee used Rugel's plantain, *P. Rugelii*, as a poultice for swellings.

The plantain was also used internally. The Paiute drank boiled root tea for colds, while the Aleuts used the same formulation as a general tonic and the Fox used it as a diuretic.

Since the 1930s the seeds of several European species of plantain have become a very popular remedy for constipation in the United States as the primary ingredient in several patent medicines (Metamucil is probably the best known brand though there are several others). The action of this drug is apparently largely mechanical, working more or less like bran.

There are, according to Pliny, certain specific dangers associated with plantain. Certain wicked Roman herbalists looking to increase business, Pliny said, had discovered that if one obtained some seeds of the plantain which had been prescribed for a patient and then planted them, the disease would recur. His advice was to be certain to keep track of your medicine to forestall this iatrogenic eventuality. Forewarned is forearmed!

## Prickly ash, the toothache tree.

### *Zanthoxylum clava-herculis*

Two species of prickly ash (members of the same family as orange and lemon trees) grow to form small trees or bushy shrubs. American prickly ash, *Zanthoxylum americanum*, had the more northern distribution, while Southern prickly ash, *Z. clava-herculis*, is found further south, from Virginia through Florida to East Texas. The most common native American use of these trees was as a treatment for toothache. The inner bark of either the trunk or root was held directly next to an aching tooth, or the bark was powdered and sprinkled on the sore spot. The Alabama, Fox, Houma, Iroquois, and Comanche all used the plant in this way. The bark is still used this way in some areas of the rural south.

The tree found many other uses as well. The Menominee in particular used the tree in a variety of ways. They included it in a compound with several other ingredients which was taken to stop convulsions, and they used a simple tea of the bark for colds and fevers. They washed a tea of the berries on the chest to relieve bronchial congestion, and the same liquid was added to any other medicine to strengthen it. They also used the pounded inner bark as a poultice for rheumatic joints. Similarly, this was a favored medicine of the Fox Indians, who, in addition to using the bark for toothache, made a thick syrup by boiling down a quantity of bark and berries. This syrup was then used as an expectorant cough syrup, or to relieve other chest diseases such as tuberculosis.

At least three tribes—the Ojibwa, Chippewa, and Comanche—gargled a tea made of the bark or berries for sore throats. The Houma of Louisiana mixed grated prickly ash root with whiskey to form a paste which they rubbed on rheumatic joints.

The bark of prickly ash was used in American medicine for several centuries. The dried bark was listed in the USP from 1820 until 1926, and in the NF from 1926 to 1947. Other plant parts were official for shorter periods. The bark was generally construed to be a useful stimulant and to be helpful when applied as a "counter-irritant" to rheumatic joints, a sort of liniment. It was also, at one

*PRICKLY ASH:* Zanthoxylum clava-herculis. *Prickly ash is a small shrub or tree (up to 25 feet) with gray or bluish bark. The edges of the leaves are either smooth or may have rounded teeth. Two small, thick spines are found on the stem at the base of each leaf cluster. The wrinkled fruits release small black seeds. The tree grows along river banks and in rich woods.*

time or another, recommended as an "emmenagogue," that is, an agent that facilitated menstruation. Taken with the fact that the Iroquois are known to have boiled down a tea of the bark, and to have drunk the liquid to promote miscarriage, it may well be that the bark has some abortifacient quality, and as such, women should be *particularly careful* if they wish to experiment with it.

Prickly ash will serve to illustrate another aspect of Indian botanical medicine. The Pawnee used prickly ash berries as a diuretic for their horses, that is, it played a role in veterinary medicine. I learned of another such case in 1970 while I was doing anthropological research among rural blacks in the Sea Islands along the coast of South Carolina. The customs of our time require that, in a scientific monograph, I report something like this: "Informants say that a decoction of the bark of *Zanthoxylum clava-herculis* is considered to be a very powerful veterinary antidiarrheal." What *really* happened was this. I was sitting around one day with one of my neighbors, an old raconteur named "Pine" Harwood, chewing tobacco, smoking cigars, and telling lies. The conversation shifted to medicinal plants, and old "Pine" told me that the "Bark of the pickle ash—it'll check-up run-stomach in cows and pigs! Can't give 'em too much, 'cause it check-em up too good... you'll cork 'em for keeps. Man, that's good stuff."

That afternoon with "Pine" Harwood was "good stuff" too.

*PUSSY WILLOW: Salix discolor. The pussy willow is readily recognized by its silky spring catkins of male flowers. The narrow, tapering, toothed leaves are three to five inches long, and have silvery undersides. Pussy willows grow to form shrubs or small trees up to 25 feet tall in swamps, damp places and thickets.*

## Pussy willow: natural aspirin.

### *Salix discolor*

Aspirin is, of course, the most commonly used synthetic drug in the western world. It is more reasonable to calculate daily intake in units of, say, freight car loads than anything else. In addition to everyday non-prescription use for headaches, colds, and fever, aspirin is the standard drug for the treatment of serious arthritis. While many other drugs are available for arthritis, none of them has a better overall anti-inflammatory action than aspirin.

Aspirin is a synthetic drug, acetylsalicylic acid, developed in the 1890's as a substitute for methyl salicylate, found in wintergreen and black birch (see our chapter on those two species). Aspirin is a somewhat more effective drug than methyl salicylate, and a good deal less toxic. The chemical precursor of all these drugs, however, is *salicin*, a chemical widely distributed in nature, particularly in the bark of species of willow. Salicin has much the same set of properties as do the other "salicylates," and can be obtained in higher or lower concentrations from almost any willow species.

I have chosen to illustrate the pussy willow because it is both widespread and charming, a pleasant addition to anyone's hedgerow. Native Americans used at least 15 to 20 different willow species, and most any of them will serve. Since the taxonomy of the willows is confused and specialists disagree on exact classifications, I will consider together the different species of *Salix*.

The Aztecs, in their inimitable fashion, called willow "Quetzalhuexotl". They used it to reduce fevers and to inhibit bleeding after childbirth.

The Eskimos use very few medicinal plants for the more or less obvious reason that there aren't very many to be had; they do use a boiled bark tea of an arctic willow as a gargle for sore throats, and the leaves of another species as a poultice for sores. In the latter practice they are joined by several other tribes—the Thompson Indians, the Ojibwa, Bella Coola, Potawatomi, and Micmac—all of whom used the bark topically on sores, cuts, wounds, and bruises. The Paiute sprinkled powdered willow bark on the newborn infant's navel to facilitate healing. Several of the salicylates are quite efficient antiseptics, which probably accounts for these widespread practices.

Several tribes used willows for headaches or rheumatism, though not as many as might be expected. To treat rheumatism, the Creek drank or bathed with a tea made of willow and spicewood, *Lindera benzoin.* The Thompson Indians used boiled willow tea as a hot bath for sore swollen feet. The Montagnais used the boiled bark tea for headache—they both drank it and bathed the aching head with the warm liquid.

The Menominee and Paiute used boiled tea of willow branches or roots as a general tonic, while the Penobscot smoked the dried bark to relieve asthma.

Willow has been used medicinally in many other parts of the world as well. In China it has been used internally for jaundice, rheumatism, hemorrhage, and fever, and externally for sores, cuts, and ulcers. It was also an important drug for the Romans—Pliny, in his monumental *Natural History* says that it was used for hemorrhages, for removing corns, for clearing the eyes, for relieving gout, and, mixed with rose oil, for soothing earaches. He adds an interesting warning: "The leaves thoroughly pounded and taken in drink check over-lustful desire; too many doses produce absolute impotence" (XXXIV 37).

This caution remembered, willow bark tea can be used in any case where you would ordinarily use aspirin. Soak a cupful of bark in a quart of water for several hours, then boil for a few moments. Strain the liquid, and take two ounces four times per day. *Do not take more than eight ounces a day.*

Pussy willow is a hardy shrub which will thrive in any but the driest soil; children love the catkins in the spring. Weeping willow, an Asian species now widespread in North America, is a beautiful tree from a distance, but has no place in a small yard since it often attracts an enormous number and variety of bugs and beetles. Perhaps the little beasts all have headaches.

## Roses, the vitamin bush.

### *Rosa woodsii*

Every health food person knows that the fruit of the rose, the rose hip, is a valuable source of vitamin C. Most don't realize that there is any more to it than that!

The rose family is one of the most important parts of the natural world for humans. Apples, plums, peaches, quinces, pears, cherries, strawberries, raspberries, blackberries, almonds, spirae, hawthorn, mountain ash, and, of course, innumerable varieties of roses, are members of this sweet family. Where would we be without them?

The root of the rose, as well as other parts of the plant including the petals, contains tannic acid, and, as we note in our chapter on sumac, this substance is a useful astringent. This accounts for most of the native American medicinal uses of roses. The Chippewa used a boiled root tea of the wild rose, *Rosa arkansana*, to wash wounds to help them quickly dry up and heal. The Paiute and Shoshone used various parts of the wild rose, *Rosa woodsii*, as poultices for sores, cuts and swellings of one sort or another. Several groups— the Chippewa, Omaha, Ojibwa, Iroquois, and Thompson Indians—made boiled teas of various plant parts, the hips, root, or bark—to make a soothing eye wash; the Chippewa found this solution particularly helpful for people with cataracts.

The Blackfoot, Paiute, Shoshone, and Cherokee used boiled rose root tea for diarrhea; the Blackfoot considered it effective but gentle enough to recommend it particularly for children.

There were other uses as well. Several groups made stimulating tonics. The Chippewa used boiled rose root tea, the Thompson Indians used boiled tea of stems for a tonic for general indisposition, and the Paiute used the boiled leaf tea to make a spring tonic, a mild but stimulating pick-me-up. The Potawatomi used boiled root tea for headaches, and several southwestern groups—the Washoe, Paiute, and Shoshone—used the boiled root or bark tea as a cold remedy.

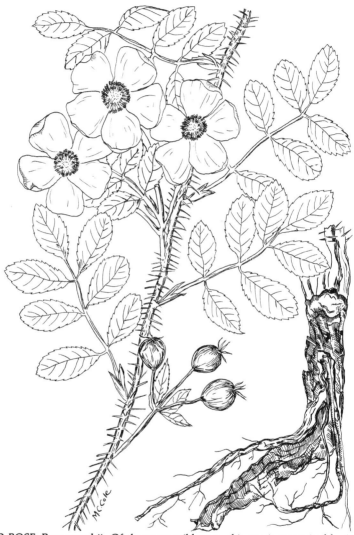

*WILD ROSE*: Rosa woodsii. *Of the many wild roses, this one is recognized by its arching prickles and oblong leaves. Wild roses are usually small shrubs with five-petalled flowers. The flowers of this species are small (about one and a quarter inches across) and pink; they form small clusters. The fruits are red. The plant is usually found on prairies and plains.*

Several species of wild rose were official in the USP from 1820 until after the turn of the century. They were used in various ways, particularly in the manufacture of rose water and rose oil. Rose water was used as a mild astringent and carminative (that is, to reduce flatulence). Rose oil, used in perfumes, is made nowadays in Europe, particularly in Bulgaria, by distilling the flower petals gathered in the spring. To make one pound of oil, you need a ton and a half of petals; not a cheerful prospect! The Roman natural historian Pliny tells of what is perhaps the most extraordinary medicinal use of roses. A woman had a dream of how she sent word to her son, a soldier in the praetorian guard, that he should drink water in which the root of the rose was boiled. Considering this an important omen, she proceeded to send the boy a letter pleading with him to do as the dream suggested. Now it seems the son had, without his mother's knowledge, been bitten by a dog. The letter arrived just as he was beginning to show the first symptoms of "horror of water," or hydrophobia. Taking the heaven-sent advice of his mother, the soldier was saved, as, adds Pliny, were many others who subsequently tried this cure.

Few today would have much confidence in rose water for rabies. Indeed, there are more convenient astringents available which do not require you to uproot your rose bushes. But one needs not root up his flowers to enjoy the tangy hips with their rich content of vitamin C. Wild fresh rose hips contain from 500 to 1000 milligrams of vitamin C in each 100 grams of fruit, perhaps 5 or 10 milligrams per fruit. Hence you can get your recommended daily allowance of 60 milligrams by eating a half dozen or so of the hips. Do not, however, be misled and pay the exorbitant price for dried rose hips at the drug or health food store. From half to 90% of the vitamin is destroyed when the fruits are dried. The value of wild rose hips is as a source of the vitamin, fresh, in the woods, when you are far from such commercial supplies. Enjoy the tart taste of a handful, and, Pliny to the contrary, keep your distance from rabid animals!

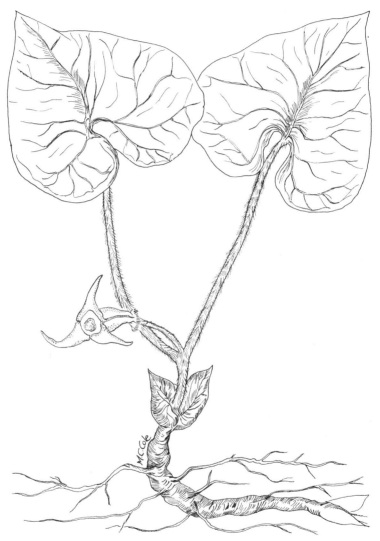

*WILD GINGER:* Asarum canadense. *The unusual flower of the wild ginger is unique in color and form. When mature, the purple-brown, three-lobed flower nods between the hairy stalks of two large, heart-shaped leaves. This six to twelve-inch-tall plant forms thick colonies in rich woods.*

## Snakeroots, Canadian and Virginian.

### *Asarum canadense*

I do not know how many different plants have at one time or another been called "snakeroot," but there certainly have been plenty. There have been at least three different species called black snakeroot, two called button snakeroot, two called Sampson's snakeroot, plus Broom-snakeroot, Seneca snakeroot, white snakeroot, and Canada snakeroot, as well as three different kinds of rattlesnake root and one rattlesnake weed. I doubt seriously that any of them had any specific effectiveness against poisonous snakebites. From a broad ecological perspective, there is no particular reason why any plants should develop any chemicals to protect themselves against snakes. Such chemicals might by chance have such effectiveness, but it seems quite unlikely. Of course, plants *do* produce unlikely substances, but this seems a bit far-fetched.

While many of the species Europeans named snakeroot were used medicinally by native Americans, few of them were used for snakebites. The reverse is also true; Indians used many species for snakebite that Europeans did not. And, few species were widely used by Indians; it seems as if each tribe had one or more plants they used this way, and only rarely did other groups use the same plants in the same way, and when they did, they were very close neighbors. Thus, the Dakota, Winnebago, and Pawnee all used the purple coneflower, *Echinaceae angustifolia*, for snakebites while both the Paiute and Shoshone used turtle back, *Psathyrotes ramosissima*, false hellbore, *Veratrum californicum*, and sweetroot, a species of *Osmorhiza*. Otherwise few tribes shared their beliefs in snakebite remedies. We can take this as circumstantial evidence against any of them being very effective.

Virginia snakeroot, *Aristolochia serpentaria*, was used for snakebite by the Mohegan who applied the pounded root on the wound as a poultice. The Choctaw used a root tea of the plant for stomach aches and the Nanticoke ate the root to kill intestinal parasites. The Natchez used a boiled root tea for fevers, and the

Delaware boiled a tea of the root either alone or with wintergreen for a general tonic.

The plant was considered a valuable snakebite remedy by Europeans throughout the 18th century, and was long afterwards recognized as a bitter tonic. Under the name serpentaria, it was listed in the USP from 1820 until 1942 and recommended as a tonic, diuretic, and stimulant which would reduce fevers. I found it still in use for fevers among country people in South Carolina in 1971.

Closely related to Virginia snakeroot is the Canada snakeroot, *Asarum canadense*, also known as wild or Indian ginger. Although a reasonably common household remedy for snakebites among Europeans in the 18th century, I know of no evidence indicating that native Americans used it for that purpose. The Menominee and Chippewa used the root to aid digestion, either eating the root, or drinking boiled root tea. The Montagnais used it as a sort of panacea, adding it to specific remedies to strengthen them, or eating it to enhance generally good health. Another species, *Asarum caudatum*, was a favored remedy of several northwest coast tribes. The Bella Coola, for example, used a boiled tea of the root and leaves for headaches, stomach aches, and rheumatism.

Canada snakeroot or wild ginger was listed in the USP from 1820 until 1873 and recommended as a tonic and stimulant. Wild ginger is unrelated to the ginger of commerce which is a tropical species originally found in southeast Asia. But it does have a similar smell and taste, and can be candied in much the same way by simmering the root pieces in a sugar syrup for several hours.

Do not rely on either of these species for snakebites. Indeed, it is hard to know *what* to do about snakebites since medical authorities cannot seem to agree. The most common advice—go to a hospital for anti-venom shots—is probably best, but, in any place where one is likely today to be bitten by a snake, probably impractical. Authorities disagree on the value of the old techniques of tourniquets, razor blades, and so on. The best practice is not to get bitten in the first place. Rattlesnakes, in any case, usually give enough warning that, with some caution, bites can be avoided. In several decades of exploring the woods and deserts of North America, I have only once encountered a rattlesnake. I was portaging a canoe from one lake to another in the near north region of Ontario. My wife was behind me carrying a pack. The buzzing of a rattlesnake is an unmistakable sound. I did the correct thing—I stopped dead in my tracks, and froze. I could hardly run (with an 80 pound canoe on my back) or even turn around, so perhaps I can't say that I did it for any reason other than pure terror! The snake, a Missasauga rattler about 3 feet long, was 4 or 5 feet in front of me on the path. For 30 seconds (which seemed to last about 2 hours) we eyed one another. Then she slowly slithered off into the woods with renewed dignity (we decided later that it was a female, for no particular reason). If rattlesnakes wanted to go around biting people, they wouldn't have rattles. They want nothing to do with us, and I, for one, share the feeling. In this case perhaps more than any other, prevention if far more valuable and possible than cure.

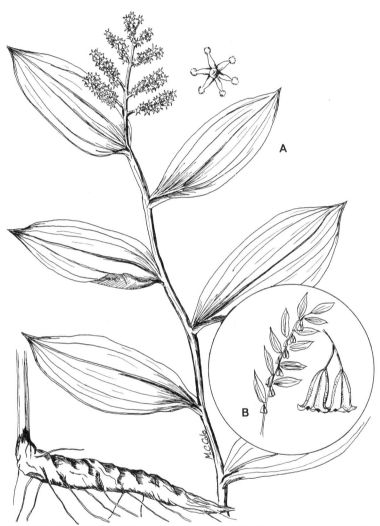

(A) *FALSE SOLOMON'S SEAL:* Smilacina racemosa. *The distinctive leaves of the False Solomon's Seal—tapered, oval-shaped, with parallel veins—are arranged alternately on a curved stem. The six pointed white flowers are arranged in a terminal cluster. Berries are ruby red.* (B) *TRUE SOLOMON'S SEAL:* Polygonatum biflorum. *True Solomon's Seal closely resembles this plant, but differs by having two flowers in the axil of each leaf, and blue-black fall berries. Both plants have knotted roots and are found growing together in thickets and rich woods.*

## Solomon's Seal: True, False, and Starry

*Polygonatum biflorum*

*Smilacina racemosa*

In the third century, we learn, the counselors of the Chinese Emperor Huangti advised him that eating the *Huang-ching*, or Solomon's Seal, would confer immortality. So far as I can tell, although many native American groups had a high regard for this plant, none of them had *this* high a regard for it.

Solomon's Seal has only a little to do with Solomon. The plant is named for the contorted shape of its rhizomes which, when sliced, appear in cross section to have the shapes of Hebrew letters. Four closely related species, *Polygonatum biflorum*, (Solomon's Seal), *P. canaliculatum* (Great Solomon's Seal), *Smilacina racemosa*, (False Solomon's Seal), and *S. stellata*, (Starry Solomon's Seal), are the members of this group of the lily family which were most widely used as medicines by native American groups. The primary difference between the two genera is that true Solomon's Seal has flowers (and, in fall, berries) springing from the stalk at the leaf axils, while False Solomon's Seal has a large cluster of Flowers (and berries) at the end of the nodding stalk. The False Solomon's Seal species were more widely used in America than the others.

The more common medicinal uses of these plants were as gynecological aids, analgesics, and wound dressings. The Ojibwa used the root of False Solomon's Seal during pregnancy to "keep the kidneys open." The Gitskan Indians used the mashed root and the Washoe used the powdered root for the same purpose. The Shoshone and Paiute used a root tea to minimize what scholars of these matters disguise as "menstrual disorders." And, as so often happens, the Shoshone case urges us to use this plant ever so carefully as we find that they used a tea of the leaf daily for a week to prevent conception for the month—one of those reports which can neither be credited *nor ignored.*

Several groups used these plants in one way or another as analgesics, or pain killers. The Thompson Indians of British Columbia used a tea of the roots of either False or Starry Solomon's

Seal to alleviate stomach pains. The Ojibwa used the root of False Solomon's Seal as a headache remedy while the Thompson Indians inhaled the steam of root tea for the same purpose. The Ojibwa used a poultice of the crushed leaves to staunch the bleeding of cuts and other wounds.

The Fox Indians burned the dried berries to form a smoke to quiet crying children. The Washoe used the root of Starry Solomon's Seal in a tea as a general tonic; the Delaware of Oklahoma used the root of False Solomon's Seal for the same purpose.

Along with the native Americans, European writers since Dioscorides have recommended the root of the Solomon's Seals to close up wounds, staunch bleeding, reduce bruises, and to hasten the healing of broken bones. As recently as 1920, Dorland's famous *American Illustrated Medical Dictionary* recommended Solomon's Seal as a "mucilaginous astringent and vulnerary," that is, an agent which would slow discharges and heal wounds. Since that time, the plant seems to have fallen from favor, perhaps because its most common use in the West (on wounds) has largely been supplanted by the notion that to stop bleeding, one should use pressure or ligature.

Although I have had no cause to learn from experience how well Solomon's Seal speeds the healing of fractured bones, I can assure you that they make a wonderful flower for a woodland garden. Several species grow thickly in the woods and fields of Michigan, and they are easily transplanted. They thrive in rich dark soil in full or dappled shade. Dig a generous measure of peat moss into the dirt around them and you will enjoy their delicate white or yellow flowers all summer and bold blue or red berries all fall. While I certainly extol their merits in the garden, I fear that I, along with the Indians and the old European herbalists, do not hold the medicinal qualities of the plant in as high regard as did the counselors of Huangti. But then again, if I did, I probably wouldn't tell you about it anyway. Sources of immortality are among those things which seem to most of us better as closely held secrets.

**Sumac and poison ivy, fighting fire with fire.**

*Rhus glabra*

*Rhus typhina*

*Toxicodendron radicans*

*Rhus toxicodendron*

It seems, at first glance, almost inconceivable that one might use poison ivy in any way as a medicine for skin diseases, but here it is!

The sumacs and poison ivy, along with the mangos, are members of the Cashew family. The family has several other members which are as toxic, perhaps even more toxic, than the ones which plague us with itching and irritation. One Cuban species is said to be so toxic that it will kill anyone who sleeps in its shade. Similarly deadly varieties occur in Southeast Asia.

The family is, nonetheless, a very useful one. In addition to providing us with cashews, several Asian species are used to produce the finest Chinese and Japanese black lacquers which give such translucent depth to Oriental furniture. A number of species also produce tannin used for tanning fine leather.

The American medicinal species are primarily smooth sumac, *Rhus glabra*, and staghorn sumac, *R. typhina*. Typically, neither of these is toxic, though some very sensitive people may have allergic reactions to them. The primary medical use of these two species was as *astringents*. An astringent is a substance which somehow precipitates proteins thus hardening the skin, forming protective coatings over mucous membranes, arresting discharges or secretions, stopping hemorrhages, in a phase, drying things up. The most common astringents in use in medicine today are metallic salts, like alum or zinc sulfate; the latter is commonly used to treat conjunctivitis, or "pink eye." It has also been used as a powder for diaper rash, but this use is no longer recommended since breathing in the powder can be very bad for the lungs.

So, the Ojibwa and Omaha used the leaves of smooth sumac in a poultice for skin irritations. The Ojibwa also used a boiled tea of

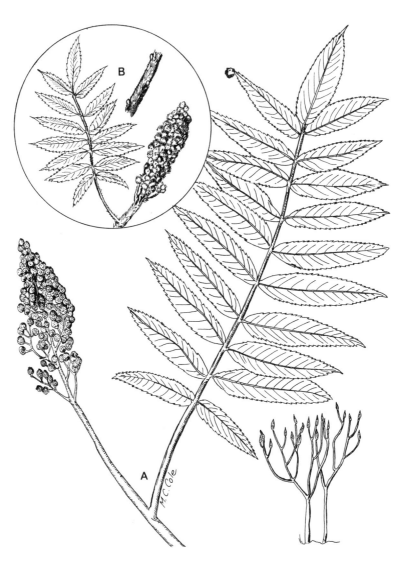

(A) *SMOOTH SUMAC*: Rhus glabra. *Smooth sumac, a shrub or, rarely, a small tree, grows to about 35 feet. The branches are smooth and the leaflets are sharply toothed. Short reddish hairs cover the crimson fruit of this plant of dry soils.* (B) *STAGHORN SUMAC*: Rhus typhina. *The dense hairs of Staghorn Sumac give the branches a velvety appearance. It is also found in rocky or dry soils.*

the root bark to stop bleeding, and a tea of the inner bark generally as an astringent. The Chippewa boiled a tea of the blossoms as a mouthwash for teething children, while the Thompson Indians chewed the root for sore mouth, tongue, or gums.

Staghorn sumac was used in a similar fashion. The Menominee found the inner bark to be a valuable remedy for hemorrhoids as did the Iroquois. Both the Mohegan and Potawatomi gargled boiled tea of the berries or leaves to relieve sore throat or tonsillitis. The Menominee made a cough syrup by boiling down a mixture of sugar and sumac berries.

Other sumac species had similar, if less frequent, uses. The root of the fragrant sumac, *Rhus aromatica*, was used by the Natchez as a poultice for boils while the Comanche used the bark in a cold remedy. Dwarf sumac, *R. copallina*, was used by the Delaware to help heal sores and boils; they also made a mouthwash of the berries.

Astringents can also help soothe some internal illnesses, notably diarrhea, and half a dozen tribes used one or another species of sumac for this problem. The Chippewa, in particular, used sumac galls in a boiled tea for this ailment. Galls are growths which appear on many species of plants, notably oaks and sumacs. They are the response of the plant to injury caused to the leaf or stem by insects or infections. Some sumac galls contain extremely high concentrations of the powerful astringent *tannin*, up to 50 or 60 percent. And it is probably the generally high tannin content of these species of sumac which accounts for most of the uses I have listed here.

The dried berries of smooth sumac were listed in the USP from 1820 until 1936 where they were recommended for these same purposes, as a sore throat gargle, astringent, and a mild stimulating tonic.

So much, for the moment, for the non-toxic species. The toxic species of the cashew family produce substances known as oleo-resins, which are the prime villains in causing the awful itching rash. Some tribes were willing to take these risks to obtain other medical benefits. Thus, the Potawatomi, recognizing that poison ivy, *Toxicodendron radicans*, was a very dangerous medicine, entrusted its use only to the most skilled medicine men who

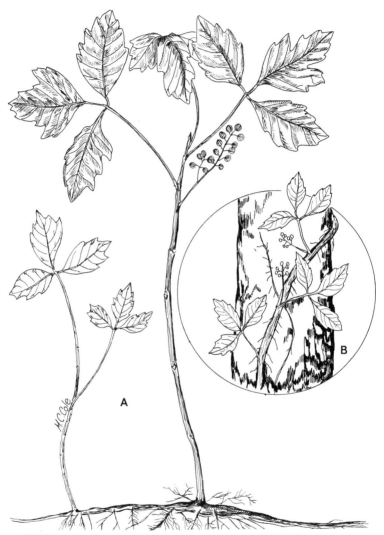

**(A)** *POISON  OAK:* Rhus toxicodendron. *Poison Oak is a small shrub-like plant with leaves shaped like those of the white oaks. The berries are yellow or white; in the fall, the foliage turns a brilliant red. The plant grows in dry barren soils and sandy places.*
**(B)** *POISON  IVY:* Toxicodendron radicans. *Poison Ivy is a climbing vine with shiny leaves in clusters of three. The vines attach themselves to trees with aerial clinging roots. The berries are greyish or white. It grows many places where it is not wanted.*

pounded the root to make a poultice used to open and drain swellings. Similarly, the Delaware used pounded poison ivy root in a salve for swollen glands and sores. The Houma, in an even more dramatic case, drank a boiled poison ivy leaf tea as a tonic and stimulating rejuvenator. Odd as this may seem, such a use was at least considered possible in 19th century professional American medicine. From 1820 until 1905, the leaves of poison oak, *Rhus toxicodendron*, were listed in the USP as a stimulant and narcotic! There is no accounting, as they say, for taste.

Can we account for the experience involved? Consider the testimony of Charles Millspaugh, a great 19th century botanist-physician. His famous work *American Medicinal Plants* published in 1892 is a fascinating compendium of information on botany and medicine. Writing of smooth sumac, he first describes the quite horrible reaction of one individual to a huge dose of a tincture (alchol extraction) of sumac bark: headache, hemorrhage of the nose, ulceration of the mouth, diarrhea, weariness, fatigue, great loss of flesh, etc., etc. He continues:

> One sympton was also developed (in this poor sufferer) that I desire to comment upon, viz.: "dreams of flying through the air." During the summer of 1879, while botanizing near Bergin Point, N. J., I came into a swarm of furious mosquitos; quickly cutting a large branch from a sumac bush at hand, I used it vigorously to fight off the pests. Several fine specimens of Baptisia tinctoria grew at hand, and while studying them I kept the sumac branch in constant motion, perspiring freely during the time. On leaving the spot I cut a cane from the same shrub, and also ate of the refreshing berries. For three successive nights following this occurrence I flew (!) over the city of New York with a graceful and delicious motion that I would give several years of my life to experience in reality. Query: Did I absorb from my perspiring hands sufficient juice of the bark to produce the effect of the drug, or was it from the berries I held in my mouth? I noticed no other symptoms, and never before or since enjoyed a like dream.

The one common feature of several hallucinogens seems to be that they induce visions of flying (see our discussion of Jimson-weed). Is there some possibility that some of the sumacs have a similar property? I do not know, and given my childhood experiences with the shiny leaved members of this group, I am not about to find out!

The limits of my personal use of these plants is sumac tea, or "Indian lemonade," a cool mildly stimulating drink made by covering several bunches of ripe red berries with cold water, mashing them with a potato masher, or whatever is handy, and straining the liquid through several layers of cloth or through a coffee filter. The tart pink liquid is a refreshing pick-me-up, particularly when you are far from home in the fall woods. A hot foot bath of boiled stems will also soothe blistered feet on the same hike. Just be certain to pick the sumacs with *red* berries, not white ones, and you will be alright. Otherwise, you are likely not to fight the fire, but feed it, turning a little blister into the mess of your life!

## Sweet cicely, consumer of wind.

### *Osmorhiza claytonii*

Many of the drugs we have considered here were widely used by both European and Native Americans. Some European plants introduced to North America were rapidly taken up by Indians, and, of course, the reverse of that process often occurred. Here, however, is a case where that didn't happen. Sweet cicely was a drug with wide use in North America, particularly in the southwest, which was rarely used by Euro-Americans, and never became a part of professional medicine.

As the technical classification of the species of the genus *Ozmorhiza* is complex, engendering disagreement among specialists, I will not attempt to differentiate the half dozen more or less similar species; they all have the same medicinal value.

Several tribes used the anise-scented root of sweet cicely as a dressing for cuts, sores, boils or wounds. The Chippewa, Omaha, Winnebago, Paiute and Shoshone used the mashed root, either raw or dried and powdered, on such wounds. The Paiute and Shoshone used the mashed raw roots as a dressing for snake bites. The Paiutes also used boiled root tea to wash sores or cuts. The Menominee, Fox, Potawatomi, Paiute and Shoshone all used boiled root tea as a wash to soothe red, irritated eyes.

The root was also used internally for a variety of illnesses like colds, sore throats, fevers, stomach aches and indigestion. The Tlingit, for example, used a boiled tea of the roots and leaves as a cough medicine. The Shoshone and Washoe used boiled root tea for stomach aches as did the Paiutes who also chewed the root slowly to soothe sore throats. The Pawnee used boiled root tea for weakness and general debility, to build up anyone who was not feeling well. In stronger doses, the southwestern tribes found sweet cicely to be a useful cathartic while the Bella Coola considered it a helpful emetic. The Fox Indians were perhaps the most enthusiastic users of this plant; they considered it to be good for everything!

Sweet cicely is a member of the parsley family which includes many well known plant species, among them parsley, chervil,

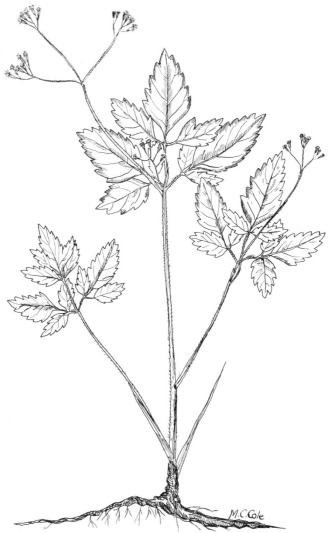

*SWEET CICELY:* Osmorhiza claytonii. *The fragrant root of this plant has the odor of licorice. It grows from one-and-a-half to four feet tall, and has broad, deeply toothed, fernlike leaves in groups of three. Small white flowers are clustered at the ends of thin, slightly hairy stalks. It is found in woodlands and clearings.*

coriander, anise, caraway, dill, fennel, parsnips and carrots. Among the less pleasant members of the family is poison hemlock, *Conium maculatum,* the species used by the ancient Greeks to execute criminals, including Socrates.

Like many of these kitchen herbs, the root of sweet cicely smells of anise; it is sometimes known as anise root. Many of these species probably contain some of the same principles in their aromatic oils, and have similar medicinal properties. All of them (except poison hemlock!) have been used medicinally to one degree or another. Among the most curious is the carrot. Most people can recognize the ordinary garden carrot with its frilly green leaves, and many can also recognize Queen Anne's Lace, a tall rangy weed which grows along roadsides and in neglected fields. But few realize that they are the same species, *Daucus carota.* Carrots are a biennial species, that is, they grow a large root the first year and only produce flowers and seeds the second year. Our garden carrots never last that long! Indeed, the cultivated varieties are a long way from the wild ones with their tough stringy first year roots. Carrot seeds are an old folk remedy for what is politely known as "flatulence," or "gas." In fact, many of these plants are effective "carminatives," that is, anti-flatulence agents. And this may be why sweet cicely never worked its way into Euro-American medicine. The standard European carminative of this group is anise, *Pimpinella anisum.* In 1633, Gerard said that anise seed "consumeth wind," phrasing it rather nicely. In any event, the Europeans seem to have stuck with their anise, while the Indians seem to have stuck with their sweet cicely.

Sweet cicely grows in woods and thickets all over North America, usually flowering in May or June. The sweetly scented root can be chewed raw, or made into a tea which will calm the stomach after a highly spiced meal. And there is at least one more use for the plant. The Iroquois make a guaranteed fishing medicine by chewing on the roots, and spitting on the bait. This is also a good carminative, since who ever heard of anyone getting gas from eating a nice fresh fish?

*SWEETFLAG:*   Acorus calamus. *The erect, one to six-foot-tall sword-shaped leaves of this plant rise from a thick creeping horizontal rootstalk. The spadix of tightly packed flowers juts at an angle from the stalk. Sweetflag is a perennial plant found in wet meadows, shores and pond edges.*

## Sweetflag, protector of children.

### *Acorus calamus*

Sweet flag, or calamus, was certainly one of the medicinal plants most widely used by native Americans. Throughout its range and beyond, it was a favored cold remedy, cough medicine, general tonic, and pain killer for colic, stomach cramps, sore throat and toothache. Some tribes traded for it with distant neighbors. The Chippewa, for example, ground the root for use as snuff or brewed a root tea; both forms were used as a cold remedy. They also gargled with the tea to relieve sore throats. In the Plains, the Dakota, Omaha, Pawnee and Winnebago chewed the root to relieve toothaches or coughs, and drank the root tea to lower fevers. The Micmac, Cheyenne, and Mohecan used the root tea or chewed the root as a general panacea, to prevent illness, or to help a sufferer of any illness regain his strength.

The Cheyenne tied small bits of root to their children's pajamas to protect them from the illnesses caused by night spirits. This is a highly recommended procedure. The lovely aroma of the sweetflag is surely as offensive to evil spirits as it is soothing to children, buffeted by the complexity of youthful days.

Sweetflag is not a native plant but was introduced early into North America, where native Americans quickly learned its virtues as it spread across the continent in wet swampy places and along rivers and lakes. It has a long medical history in Europe and Asia where it was deemed useful for preventing obesity, enhancing digestion, and relieving cold symptoms. Indeed, in a use similar to that of the Cheyenne, Moses, in Exodus, 30, tells us how God directed him to formulate a holy oil containing calamus which was to be used to anoint the tabernacle, the ark of the testimony and other ritual paraphernalia. He was instructed to use the balm to anoint Aaron and his sons to consecrate them for their ministry to the Lord. The oil was to be formulated of five hundred shekels each of myrrh and cassia (a shekel is about a third of an ounce), plus half that much sweet cinnamon and sweet calamus mixed with a hin (about a gallon and a half) of olive oil. One cannot, unfortunately,

recommend the contemporary formulation of this balm since God
continued by saying that Moses should do this only once, and that
anyone else who made the compound or put any on a stranger
"shall even be cut off from his own people." In any event, the
simpler Cheyenne recommendation is probably just as effective.
Some scholars argue that Moses' calamus was not our sweetflag,
but ginger-grass, *Andropogon aromatica*, a sweet scented member
of the grass family native to India. Since the argument is purely
circumstantial, and since ginger-grass is unavailable, I prefer the
other interpretation.

The plant flowers from May until August in damp areas, along
rivers and lake shores. One to four feet tall, it has long sabre-like
leaves with a golden spadix—a rod-shaped stalk covered with
many tiny florets.

The rather distinctive shape of the flower probably accounts for
its symbolic use in the "calamus cluster" of poems by Walt
Whitman in *Leaves of Grass*; these poems celebrate what Whitman
called "adhesiveness ... a personal attachment between men that is
stronger than ordinary friendship," phrasing more eliptical than
that of the poems themselves.

The root, actually a rhizome, should be collected in the fall and
dried in the sun. Only a lucky few will have the damp conditions
suitable to its cultivation. When nearly dry, the rhizome might be
refrigerated—then small pieces can be chewed in place of the usual
after dinner mints (not, of course, to avoid the mint (*c.f.*), but the
sugar). Or, the sun dried material can be chopped like an onion,
and made into an after dinner tea. Used in moderation, perhaps as
a supplement to a prepared cinnamon tea, this seems a more
civilized way to enjoy the herb (there being nothing to spit out
afterwards!)

As is always the case, a word of caution is in order. At least three
native American groups are reported to have used calamus for
"irregular periods," or "suppressed menses." There is some
possibility, in other words, that the plant may act as an abortifacient. Pregnant women should always be careful of the drugs that
they take, and herbal medicines are no different. I would certainly
not rely on calamus as a method for inducing abortion; but were I
pregnant, I would certainly avoid the plant. Only after the babe

were born would I protect its nights with the sweet root attached to
the bedclothes.

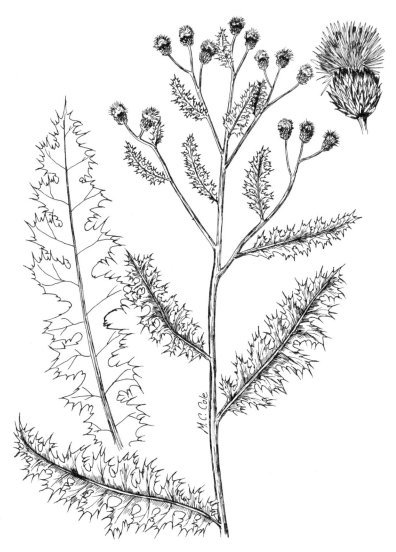

*THISTLE:* Cirsium arvense. *This two to six-foot-tall plant has showy, lilac-colored flowers surrounded by flattened bracts. Deeply lobed leaves with bristly spines are arranged alternately on a smooth stem. The thistle is a common plant of waste places, fields and meadows.*

## The paradoxical thistles.

### *Cirsium arvense*

The thistle is a combination of opposites, a paradoxical plant. The foliage is rank, repelling: prickly, angular, unkept. The blooms are transcendent: unearthly red, a groomed mass of infinitesimally small single flowers combine to form a composite whole sharing the order of a drill team and the beauty of a symphony.

The ancient Europeans considered their thistles to be useful medicines. The generic term, *Cirsium*, is derived from Dioscorides name for the plant, Cirsion, from the Greek word *circos* meaning "a swollen vein" which the thistles were reputed to heal. The old herbalists considered them to be useful as well. Gerard found that the root tea made a diuretic which cleansed the body of "ranke and rammish sauor (savor, or smell)." He added that it reduced the "ranke smell of the arme-holes," a sixteenth century underarm deodorant.

Native Americans used a half-dozen species of thistle in a variety of ways. The common thistle, *Cirsium arvense*, an introduced European species, was used by the Mohegan as a soothing mouthwash for infants; they washed the child's mouth with a cooled leaf tea. The Ojibwa used the common thistle as a tonic for sore bowels while the Montagnais drank boiled thistle leaf tea for tuberculosis. The Delaware used a tea of the bull thistle, *Cirsium vulgare*, another introduced species, as a liniment for arthritis.

The Navajo used roots of two indigenous species, the lavender thistle, *C. neomexicanus*, and the wavy-leaved thistle, *C. undulatum*, in a tea to bathe sore eyes of people or livestock. Both species were also included in the complex "life-medicine" of the Navajo which was a panacea, insurance for excellent health. Various other species of thistle were used by the Chippewa for a number of women's problems, by the Hopi for sore throats and for itching, by the Houma as an expectorant, and by the Comanche for venereal disease.

Given this long and broad tradition, it is surprising that the thistles never became part of early American medicine. It was never official and, though it was occasionally used as a folk remedy, never became a part of professional medicine.

Several species of thistle have edible roots or stems. But perhaps the most edible part of the thistles is not the roots and not for humans. On a brilliant summer day in the Black Hills of South Dakota, the mountain meadow was ablaze with brilliant thistles. Yet they were practically invisible. Hundreds of golden butterflies—mostly monarchs and viceroys—sat atop the flowers, long proboscises reaching deep into the flowers, feeding on the rich nectar. As many as five butterflies jostled one another on a single thistle. Those vivid lavender flowers were obscured by living golden crowns.

## Trillium and Wild Onion: Medicinal lilies.

*Trillium grandiflorum*

*Allium stellatum*

The lily family produces some of nature's most beautiful flowers. It also produces a great variety of medicinal plants. We have elsewhere considered the Solomon's Seals which are simultaneously beautiful and medicinal. But few medicinals are more beautiful than the trillium or wake-robin, *Trillium grandiflorum*. Walking in eastern woods in May, ablaze with the glorious white or pink flowers, with companion species of painted or red trillium with their vivid crimson blooms is an absolutely arresting experience. Native Americans found a number of uses for the roots of these beautiful flowers. The Chippewa developed an interesting technique similar to injections using trillium. They ground and boiled the roots, and then washed rheumatic joints with the liquid. Then they pricked the skin with a needle a number of times to get the liquid into the system.

The Menominee used the root tea as a diuretic. They also found it useful in several ways regarding sex and sexual problems. Women used the root tea for cramps and for irregular menstruation while men used it to cleanse themselves from the defilement they presumed to occur after having intercourse with a menstruating woman.

The Menominee also used the grated root as a poultice for sore eyes; similarly, the Thompson Indians sprinkled the dried powdered root of Pacific trillium, *T. ovatum*, in sore eyes.

The purple trillium, *T. erectum*, was listed in the NF from 1916 until 1947 and used as an astringent for diarrhea and a tonic as well as a uterine stimulant. One must remember *always* to treat uterine stimulants with the most careful discretion. A large number of other members of the lily family were also used by native Americans for various uterine problems, underscoring this caution. The Navajo used the crag-lily, *Anthericum torreyi*, mariposa, *Calochortus gunnisonii*, and beargrass, *Yucca glauca*, all members of the lily family, to ease delivery of the placenta after childbirth.

**(A)** *TRILLIUM:* Trillium grandiflorum. *A single stem, rising from a tuber-like rootstalk, supports a whorl of three broad, parallel-veined leaves. A single two to four-inch showy white flower (which turns pink with age) terminates the stem. The 12 to 18-inch tall plants are found in rich woods in the spring.*

**(B)** *WILD ONION:* Allium stellatum. *The Wild Onion, an eight to eighteen-inch narrow-leaved plant, has either one or a few clustered bulbs under ground. The small flowers are arranged in a terminal clump. It is usually found on rocky banks.*

They considered the first of these to be an aphrodisiac. The Ojibwa used the corn-lily *Clintonia borealis*, to aid childbirth; they used the Canadian mayflower, *Maianthemum canadense*, similarly, saying that it "kept the kidneys open" during childbirth. The Tewa used yucca, *Yucca baccata*, to promote easy childbirth. Perhaps the most dangerous of these members of the lily family is the false hellebore, *Veratrum californicum*, which was used for many purposes by the Shoshone, Washoe, and Paiute. Among other things, the poisonous root was used as a liniment for rheumatic joints, as a treatment for bad colds, as an antiseptic for wounds, as an emetic, and as a treatment for snakebites and venereal diseases. The Paiute also asserted that the boiled root tea of false hellebore, taken as a contraceptive, would insure permanent sterility! Similar, if less drastic, is the Navajo notion that drinking the juice of the rotten roots of beargrass induced menopause. All in all, the conclusion here is that these various lily species may very well have some significant uterine effects; they might be able to induce abortions, and, as such, should be dealt with *very carefully*.

And yet, paradoxically, most of us regularly eat large quantities of *other* members of the lily family, particularly those of the genus *Allium*, the onion, *A. Cepa*, the garlic, *A. sativum*, the leek, *A. Porrum*, and the shallot, *A. ascalonicum*. I am unaware of any evidence suggesting that these species have any uterine effects (thank goodness) although most of them were used as medicines as well as foods and flavorings. These are all European or Asian species, but there are also over 70 species of *Allium* indigenous to North America, several of which were used medicinally. The Chippewa, for example, used the wild onion, *A. stellatum*, as a cold remedy, and the boiled root tea of the wild leek, *A. tricoccum*, as an emetic. The Iroquois used the wild leek as a spring tonic to "clean out the system" and as an anthelmintic for children, while the Cherokee used the warmed juice of the plant topically for ear-aches, and ate it for colds and coughs. The Cherokee also used wild garlic, *A. canadense*, in a variety of ways, as a stimulant, an anthelmintic for children, and as a mild laxative.

The common European species were used similarly. There is evidence to show that the ancient Egyptians exploited the anti-fungal and antibacterial properties of the garlic which they used, along with several other plants, to embalm mummies. The virtues of various *Allium* species against intestinal parasites have been known for centuries in Europe as well as America. Garlic, *A. sativum,* was listed in the USP from 1820 to 1905 and in the NF from 1916 to 1936 where it was recommended as a diuretic, expectorant and as an aid to digestion.

Again, we have a group of plants whose medicinal used are best left in the past, but whose presence in the garden is most welcome. In addition to the many lilies available commercially, trillium is quite easily transplanted and grown in woodland gardens. It requires a thick organic soil and open shade; with modest care the plants will thrive and multiply, eclipsing in beauty (if not showiness) the other early bulbs—the tulips and daffodils—in your garden.

Wormwood, Mugwort, Sagebrush and
Tarragon: The Legacy of Artemis.

*Artemisia frigida*

*Artemisia glauca*

*Artemisia tridentata*

*Artemisia ludoviciana*

*Artemisia absinthium*

*Artemisia dracunculoides*

The genus *Artemisia* is the source of a great plethora of medicines. Two dozen native American groups used at least 15 species
of *Artemisia* in at least 150 different ways to treat everything from
snakebite to toothache. We will consider several widely used
species in turn.

Prairie sage, *Artemisia frigida*, is, in the first place, not sage. The
sage of our kitchens which goes into chicken stuffing is *Salvia
officinalis*, a European member of the mint family. Prairie sage was
a particularly favored medicine of the Chippewa who used it as a
cure for "fits" or convulsions, as a coagulant for wounds, as a
stimulant and tonic, and as a cure for nausea or biliousness.
Women in several Plains tribes—the Dakota, Omaha and
Pawnee—used a boiled leaf tea to regulate menstruation, while the
Blackfoot chewed the leaves for heartburn. The Navajo used the
leaf tea as a cough medicine.

The "fuzzy weed," *Artemisia glauca*, also known as false
tarragon, was also highly favored by the Chippewa who used it in a
strengthening bath for infants, as a poultice for wounds, as an aid
during childbirth when labor was prolonged, and as a heart
medicine (the leaves were chewed); in addition, they added the
leaves to a mixture used as a shampoo which, they said, made hair
grow. The Thompson Indians used it in a tea which they washed on
the head and temples for headache. They also placed the plant on

(A) *PRAIRIE SAGE:* Artemisia frigida. *Prairie sage is readily recognized by its silky lower leaves which form thick mats. Small flower heads grow on the 10 to 20-inch-tall stems which are covered with narrowly divided leaves. The plant is found in rocky soils and on dry plains.*

(B) *FUZZY WEED:* Artemisia glauca. *Fuzzy weed does not have the mat-forming leaves. The stems are hairier than those of the prairie sage, and the lower leaves are consistently divided in threes. The plant has a similar habitat.*

the hot rocks in their steam baths to alleviate the pain of arthritis. The Winnebago, like the Thompson Indians, sprinkled the leaf tea on the head for headaches. They also chewed the roots and rubbed the resulting mass on their clothes to make a love medicine to attract members of the opposite sex.

The Western Mugwort, *Artemisia ludoviciana*, was a favored remedy in the Southwest, particularly of the Paiute and Shoshone. Both tribes used the plant as an analgesic and antidiarrheal, as a wash for rashes or sores, as an eyewash, to reduce fevers, for stomach aches, and for headaches and fevers expecially for infants. The Fox also used the leaves as a poultice for wounds, but the Ojibwa found the herb to be particularly helpful for treating the ailments of their horses.

Another member of the genus, the big sagebrush, *Artemisia tridentata*, was commonly used in the Southwest, again particularly by the Shoshone (who used the leaves for toothaches) and the Paiute, but by several other groups as well. The Coahuilla of Southern California used a tea of the plant for stomach aches as did the Hopi and Tewa. The Navajo applied the wet leaves to rheumatic joints and used the leaf tea for a cough medicine and for postpartum pain in new mothers. Both the Washoe and Thompson Indians used the plant in a tea which they drank for colds.

At least ten other *Artemisia* species were used medicinally by native Americans. Five different species were used by various groups for rheumatism. The Eskimo, for example, applied the leaves of *A. tilesii* to rheumatic joints. Several other tribes used various species for boils and sores; the Hopi used silver sage, *A. filifolia*, on boils; they, along with the Tewa, used the same species in several different ways for indigestion, while the Navajo used it for snakebite. The Aleuts used *A. unalaskensis* as a poultice on wounds and sores.

Although none of these American species of Artemisia have been official drugs, a very famous (or infamous) European species, *A. absinthium*, was long in the pharmacopoeia (USP, 1831-1901, NF, 1916-1926). This species, known both as wormwood and absinthe, has been used medicinally at least since the time of the Greeks, and probably since long before them. Pliny, noting that it was specifically useful for the troubles of women (an opinion shared by

(A) *BIG SAGEBRUSH:* Artemisia tridentata. *The unusual leaves of Big Sagebrush have three to seven teeth at the widened leaf tip. This silvery shrub grows from 1 to 12 feet tall and is found in rocky soils and on dry plains.*
(B) *WESTERN MUGWORT:* Artemisia ludoviciana. *The Western Mugwort is shorter, from two to four feet, with toothless, tapering, woolly leaves. The stems are also woolly, and are branched near the top. It too is found in dry soils.*

several native American groups, and one to which we shall return), states further that the plant, when taken mixed with wine, counter-acted the effects of opium! This utterly unlikely position may be precisely backwards! Absinthe, a liquor made by distilling a mixture of wine and wormwood, was banned by many western nations around the turn of the century when it became apparent that the drink frequently caused serious addiction and debility including intense gastro-intestinal distress, nervousness, stupor, convulsions, and even death, as it seriously upset the entire nervous system. The only alcoholic version of wormwood still in wide use is vermouth, a white wine flavored with wormwood and other herbs; note that the word "vermouth" is derived from the 8th century Old English word "wermod," or "wormwood." A martini, made of gin (alcohol flavored with juniper berries) and vermouth (wine flavored with wormwood), is a most medicinal concoction, overwhelming evidence, perhaps, of the simultaneous blessings and curses associated with the genre.

In a contemporary world, few of these native American medicinal uses of the Artemisias can be recommended. In particular, women should be *particularly careful* with wormwoods: at least four different species of *Artemisia* were used by native Americans, in the curious euphemisms of turn-of-the-century researchers, to "regulate menstruation," to control "irregular menstruation," to correct "stoppage of periods," all of which translate into a more modern idiom as to "terminate pregnancy." The species most closely associated with these uses has been mugwort, *Artemisia vulgaris*. Hippocrates, in particular, noted its special utility in stimulating uterine contractions and the like. The source of the generic term has been a matter of controversy for two millenia: some say it is named after Artemisia, the politically powerful wife (and apparently also sister!) of Mausolus, a king of Caria (in present day Anatolia) in the 4th century BC (the tomb she built for him was called the Mausoleum); others say that the name comes directly from Artemis, the patroness of love. Either case supports this ancient association with gynecology and underscores the potential dangers associated with these plants.

There are several *Artemisia* varieties which have taken a

(A) *ABSINTHE:* Artemisia absinthium. *The lower leaves of Absinthe are deeply cut and fern like. By contrast, the upper leaves are linear and unlobed. Both sets of leaves are whitish and silky on both sides. This one to three-foot-tall aromatic plant frequents waste places.*

(B) *TARRAGON:* Artemisia dracunculus. *Tarragon is similar in habit to Absinthe, but only rarely has the deeply cut lower leaves. It is a two to four-foot tall plant of plains, dry prairies, and herb gardens.*

deserved place in the garden. Two of particular merit are Silver Mound and Southernwood, both of which are prized as border plants for their silvery-green foliage. But one additional species stands out as, in my opinion, the single most important plant for the kitchen, the most essential culinary herb of them all. This is the French tarragon, *Artemisia dracunculus* var. *sativa*, without which cooked carrots are a mere vegetable, but with which they are an epicure's salvation, without which vinegar is acetic acid, but with which it is an elixir to make a salad sing. The French tarragon is a curious plant which does not propagate from seeds, but which must be grown from roots or cuttings in order to get leaves with the unique licoricy tang. You can't tell by looking: Russian tarragon looks identical, but you might as well add grass stems to your stock. If you want to purchase a plant, crumble a leaf and sniff it—the odor is as unmistakable as it is wonderful. The perennial plant forms a shrubby bush two or three feet tall. Let it grow until late fall, until it is almost dried out. Then clip off 5 or 6 stems, gently roll them between your hands, and force them into a gallon jug of white vinegar. Let it stand for a month or so before you start to use this superb condiment in your salad dressings, barbecue sauces, and relishes.

The names of tarragon refer to *its* medieval medicinal values; both "tarragon" and "dracunculus" are derived from the Greek work *drakon*, dragon, and allude to the utility of the plant in protecting one from the bites of the great heraldic beasts. I can attest to this tradition; I regularly consume the herb, and I have never once been bitten by a dragon. Q. E. D.

*YARROW:* Achillea millefolium. *The frilly, fern-like leaves of Yarrow are arranged alternately along an upright stem. Near the top of the plant, the stem branches to support crowded clusters of tiny white flowers. Yarrow is a plant of fields and roadsides.*

## Yarrow: Achilles, Shanidar, and perhaps beyond.

### *Achillea millefolium*

The fleet has gathered in Aulis, one thousand and thirteen ships; Agamemnon and Achilles share command. They head for Troy, but lose their way. Finding themselves in Mysia, they lay waste to the countryside. Telephus, king of the Mysians, son of Hercules, rallies his people and wins the day, routing the Greek multitude, all but swift-footed Achilles, who rushes at the brave king. Telephus, fleeing, trips over a vine. Achilles wounds him in the thigh with his great sword. But to little avail.

The loss is extraordinary. The fleet is dispersed in a great storm. Eight years pass. The fleet reassembles, but no one can lead it to Troy. Telephus in Mysia is in pain; in these eight years his wound has not healed. Apollo tells him that cure can only come from the one who wounded him. Telephus goes to Achilles. Heal my wound, he says, and I will direct you to Troy.

The war depends on Achilles skill as a healer. The son of Thetis, a sea nymph, and Peleus, king of the Myrmidons, Achilles was raised by Chiron, the centaur, teacher of Asklepios, the first physician. Fed by Chiron on the organs of the lion and wild boar, on the marrow of bears, all to give him courage, and on honey and fawn's marrow to make him run swiftly, Achilles was raised to be a warrior; but raised by Chiron, he knew his medicine as well.

Into Telephus' wound, he scraped some copper-rust from his sword, the same one with which Telephus was wounded. And atop that, he lay leaves of a plant whose healing virtues he discovered, which is named after him, *Achillea*, or yarrow. Telephus, cured, directed the fleet to Troy, and the epic battle could begin in earnest. Such, at least, is the testimony of Pliny and Apollodorus, Hyginus and Homer.

But now we know that at least some of the virtues of *Achillea* were appreciated by men long before the time of Homer, before the time even of Zeus, before men invented agriculture, before they painted the walls of caves. From the Middle Paleolithic site of Shanidar in Iraq, in strata 60,000 years old, Ralph Solecki and his colleagues excavated a Neanderthal burial known as Shanidar IV, apparently an adult female. From an analysis of the surrounding soils by Arlette Leroi-Gourhan, of the Musée de l'Homme in Paris, we learn the extraordinary truth: Shanidar IV (someone's mother, or sister, or lover) was buried in this ancient cave lying on a bower of spring flowers—blue cornflowers, St. Barnaby's thistle, groundsel, grape hyacinths, joint fir, and, of course, yarrow. All of these species are still used medicinally today in the Middle East. Elsewhere in this book is a discussion of joint fir, *Ephedra,* as it was used by both native Americans and ancient Chinese.

I do not know if these Neanderthals, the very earliest members of our species, used these plants medicinally. That they had some sense of medicine is probably to be drawn from the fact that another fossil from the same Shanidar cave represents the mortal remains of a crippled old man, who, in all likelihood, had his right arm amputated below the elbow long before the roof of the cave fell in on top of him—creating a condition beyond the capacities of the Neanderthals, or us, to cure.

Sixty thousand years is a long time. Fifty seven thousand seven hundred years after Shanidar IV died, Pericles spoke in Athens. A mere twenty three hundred years after that, the words of the great Athenian democrat seem to us ancient and remote. And yet the traditions of Shanidar lived on into our own times in the indigenous medicine of the new world.

Yarrow was naturalized in North America very early, and the plant spread widely and fast. Native Americans quickly learned of its virtues, and adopted if for a wide range of uses. The most common use, as for Achilles, was as a dressing for wounds. The Thompson Indians used a boiled tea of the foliage for irritated skin, while the Menominee used a fresh leaf poultice for children's rashes. The Chippewa used a boiled root tea for rashes, while the Winnebago used a milder leaf tea to bathe swellings and sores, or used the dried crumbled leaves as a dusting powder for the same irritations. They also used a mild tea or a crumbled leaf for earaches, the former as a soothing wash and the latter as you or I might use a wisp of cotton. The Thompson Indians used boiled leaf tea as an eyewash.

The plant was also used internally for a number of different ailments. The boiled leaf tea was drunk by the Carrier Indians as a cold remedy, by the Menominee and Montagnais to lower fevers, and used as a gargle for sore throats by the Gitskan. The Thompson Indians used leaf tea as a generally stimulating tonic, while the Mohegan considered such a tonic particularly effective for liver and kidney disorders.

The Creek used the plant to relieve toothaches. The Bella Coola used the chewed leaves as a burn dressing while the Zuni used a closely related species, *Achillea lanulosa*, as a wash or mouthwash before exhibitions of fire walking or fire swallowing (at which they were particularly adept!)

Although yarrow was a common household remedy in America, it was not a favorite of professional physicians. The plant was briefly listed in the USP (from 1863 to 1882), and has not been closely examined by pharmacologists. It is, however, one of the very oldest known human medicines, and, in this ancient tradition, we stand with great predecessors—the Neanderthals of Shanidar, the centaur Chiron, swift-footed Achilles, Menominees and Chippewas, aware of our mortality, angry, and fighting for our blood and lives with some of the best tools for it that the world provides: the plants that grow around us.

# Native American groups.

This list briefly identifies the native American peoples discussed in this book.

ALEUT. The Aleuts live in western Alaska and the Aleutian Islands. Like the Eskimos, the Aleuts were hunting peoples who lived primarily on marine mammals and fish. They fabricated large ocean-going skin-covered kayaks. Today, most Aleuts work at commercial fishing, or in canneries.

APACHE. The Apache are an Athabascan people of west Texas and Northern Mexico who are linguistically related to the Navajo and northeastern Chippewa. Essentially a hunting and gathering people, the Apache also cultivated some crops, primarily corn, beans and squash.

AZTEC. The Aztecs of Mexico had one of the greatest of the ancient civilizations. A vast theocratic state rivaling ancient Egypt in its monumental architecture, the Aztecs were easily conquered by the Spanish after their population was ravaged by smallpox, introduced by the conquerors.

BELLA COOLA. A Northwest Coast tribe of British Columbia, the Bella Coola had a complex social order with "classes," traditionally labeled chiefs, nobles, commoners and slaves. Their economy was based on hunting, gathering, and primarily on fishing the rich salmon resources of the Eastern Pacific.

BLACKFOOT. The Blackfoot were a confederation of three northern plains groups, the Piegan, Blood, and "Blackfoot proper." One of the classic buffalo hunting plains tribes, the Blackfoot adopted their buffalo hunting life after they attained horses in about 1730.

*CARRIER.* The Carrier are an important tribe of inland British Columbia who lived along the great rivers of that region. They were essentially a hunting, fishing and gathering people. They now live on a number of small British Columbia reserves and are involved in both the lumbering and fur-trapping industries.

*CHEROKEE.* The Cherokee were probably the largest eastern native American group at the time of European contact with a population of about 30,000 living in the southern Appalachian region. After the defeat of their British allies in the Revolutionary War, the Cherokee essentially undertook a massive culture change to adapt themselves to new American ways. The great Cherokee scholar Sequoyah developed a written version of his language in the 1820s, and shortly thereafter most Cherokees could read and write. But soon gold was discovered on their land, and President Andrew Jackson engineered the "Cherokee removal" which resulted in the Trail of Tears, as most of the tribe was forced to walk to Oklahoma where, after terrible suffering, this resilient people prospered again.

*CHEYENNE.* The Cheyenne were an Algonquian group from the western Great Lakes region who moved onto the Northern Plains after obtaining horses in the 17th century. They organized huge communal buffalo hunts. After the 19th century Indian wars, some Cheyenne ended up in Oklahoma while others were established on reservations in Montana.

*CHIPPEWA.* In this book, the term Chippewa refers to the Ojibwa people of northern Minnesota and western Ontario. See Ojibwa.

*CHOCTAW.* A large tribe centered in Mississippi and Alabama, the Choctaw were agriculturalists who supplemented their farming with hunting and trapping. This peaceful tribe, like the Cherokee, was moved to Oklahoma, then the "Indian terri-tory," with genocidal suffering in the 1830s.

*COAHUILLA.* The Coahuilla or Cahuilla are a California group who lived in the vicinity of Palm Springs. Essentially a gathering people, the Coahuilla collected at least 60 different kinds of plants for food; their staple food, however, was acorns. Only a few hundred of these people remain on several tiny reservations.

*COMANCHE.*   See Shoshone.

*CREEK.*   The Creek or Muscogee of present day Alabama and Georgia were an agricultural people with complex democratic social institutions and a rich religious tradition. Siding with the British in the American Revolution, they suffered serious losses after the defeat of their allies. In the 1830s, most of the tribe was removed to Oklahoma.

*DELAWARE.*   The Delaware or Lenni Lenapi, as they called themselves, were a large and powerful Algonquian tribe of the Delaware Basin in present-day New Jersey, Delaware and Pennsylvania. They grew corn, beans and squash, hunted bear, deer, ducks and small game, gathered sea foods and collected nuts, herbs, roots and berries. As with other eastern tribes, the Delaware were forced westward by Europeans, first to Ohio, then to Kansas and finally to Oklahoma; some however migrated northward—their descendants live today in Ontario.

*ESKIMO.*   The Eskimo or Inuit—their name for themselves meaning "people"—are a linguistically and culturally related people occupying Arctic North America from Alaska to Greenland. The more northerly Eskimos were primarily sea-mammal hunters while the more southerly Eskimos were essentially caribou hunters. Information in this book refers primarily to Alaskan Eskimos.

*FOX.*   The Fox or Mesquaki were an Algonquian people of Minnesota. A corn-farming and hunting people, the Fox had a rich religious tradition and participated in the Midewiwin society (see Ojibwa). Today, most surviving Fox Indians live on a small reservation in Iowa.

*GITSKAN.*   The Gitskan are a division of the Tsimshian tribe of northern British Columbia and the Alaskan panhandle. See Tsimshian.

*HOPI.*   The Hopi are an agricultural Pueblo people of New Mexico. Their reservation is an island inside the Navajo reservation. The Hopi village of Oraibi, established in the 12th century, is the oldest continuously occupied town north of the Rio Grande.

*IROQUOIS.* Iroquois is a term applied to a great confederacy of six northeastern agricultural tribes, the Cayuga, Mohawk, Oneida, Onondaga, Seneca, and Tuscarora. The principles of the Iroquois confederation are said to have inspired Jefferson in his vision of a federal union; this inspiration became the basis of the United States Constitution.

*KWAKIUTL.* A related group of tribes centered on Vancouver Island in British Columbia, the Kwakiutl, whose economy was based on rich anadromous fisheries, had a very complex social structure and a rich ceremonial life. Their woodcarvings, especially masks, are famous for their intricate beauty.

*LUISEÑO.* The Luiseño are a Southern California tribe who lived in the vicinity of San Diego. They were a hunting and gathering people whose staple food was acorns which they ground into flour for bread. The tribe suffered severe decline under the influence of Spanish missionaries in the late 1700s.

*MENOMINEE.* The Menominee are an Algonquian tribe living along the border of Michigan and Wisconsin. Originally living on wild rice, fish and game, their life was dramatically changed by the fur trade. Today many Menominee live at or near the Wolf River Reservation in Wisconsin where they are involved in the forest products industry.

*MICMAC.* The Micmac are a large Algonquian tribe from Eastern Canada in Nova Scotia and Prince Edward Island. They were a hunting and gathering people who were early involved in the fur trade. Today, many Micmac work in forestry, construction and shipping.

*MOHEGAN.* The Mohegan or Pequot of Connecticut were an agricultural people who grew corn and beans, and hunted in the rich eastern forests. Caught between Colonists and the British, the Mohegan suffered severe population declines in the 17th and 18th centuries. Only a few hundred descendants of this important tribe still live in Connecticut.

*MONTAGNAIS.* The Montagnais of Eastern Quebec and Labrador were nomadic hunters and fishermen who became deeply involved in the fur trade. Their numbers were seriously reduced during that period by introduced diseases: smallpox, measles, influenza. Today many Montagnais continue hunting and fishing for a livelihood.

*NANTICOKE.* The Nanticoke were a great Eastern tribe who lived in present-day Maryland and Delaware. Forced northwest by European immigrants, they federated with the Iroquois in the mid 18th century, but, suffering further military defeats, were eventually dispersed through Eastern Canada.

*NATCHEZ.* The Natchez were a rich agricultural people living along the southern Mississippi River. They had an elaborate religion based on sun worship, and practiced highly productive agricultural techniques. After several wars with the French, and serious population decline from introduced diseases, the tribe became, in effect, extinct.

*NAVAJO.* The Navajos of Arizona and New Mexico are, today, the largest native North American group, numbering over 150,000. The Navajos migrated to the southwest from the northeast in about the 13th century. A hunting and raiding people, they learned corn agriculture from the southwestern Pueblo people. They have a rich religious heritage organized around a complex healing tradition. They are justly famous for their beautiful weaving and their stunning silver jewelry.

*NOOTKA.* The Nootka are a sea faring people of Vancouver Island in British Columbia — whalers and fishermen. They built magnificent ocean-going canoes and great cedar plank houses. They are famous for their "potlatches," gigantic feasts given by chiefs to demonstrate their wealth and generosity.

*OJIBWA.* The Ojibwa or Chippewa were a hunting and fishing people of the Great Lakes region. They carried out some corn agriculture as well; in some areas they gathered wild rice as their staple food. The Ojibwa *Midewiwin,* or Grand Medicine Society was a secret organization that functioned rather like a lodge and a university, teaching esoteric and more pragmatic medical knowledge to members. The term Ojibwa in this book refers to people from several areas in Wisconsin. See also Chippewa.

*OMAHA.* The Omaha are a Siouxan tribe of northeastern Nebraska. Living along river valleys, they constructed large earth lodges to live in. They grew crops in the river bottom lands and hunted buffalo. Most Omahas today live on their reservation in northeastern Nebraska.

*PAIUTE.* The Paiute are a hunting and gathering people of the southern Great Basin in Nevada and Utah. Collecting seeds and hunting small animals (especially rabbits) was supplemented by some irrigation agriculture. The Paiute have a rich mythological tradition, and had shamans who led ceremonies and healed the sick.

*PAPAGO.* The Papago were a hunting and gathering people of the Arizona deserts. Under the influence of Catholic missionaries for several hundred years, the Papago have none-the-less retained much of their traditional religion and medicine. Healing is both herbal and spritual, the latter based on a complex collection of powerful songs. See Pima.

*PAWNEE.* The Pawnee, originally an agricultural and hunting people of the southwest, became one of the classic mounted buffalo hunting plains tribes after obtaining horses in the early part of the 18th century. They had a complex religious tradition with great ceremonies and large numbers of priests and shamans. They ceded their Nebraska territory to the United States in the 1870s; most Pawnees today live in Oklahoma.

*PENOBSCOT.* The Penobscot were a hunting, fishing and gathering people of Maine. As with other northeastern tribes, the Penobscot became involved in the fur trade and subsequently suffered in the battles between the French and British, into which they were necessarily drawn. About a thousand Penobscot now live on their reservation in Maine.

*PIMA.* The Pima were a sedentary branch of the Papago who lived along the Salt and Gila rivers in Arizona. Primarily agriculturalists, the Pima grew corn, beans and squash as well as cotton and other crops. Generally more acculturated than their Papago neighbors, about 12,000 Pimas live on several reservations near Tucson.

*POTAWATOMI.*   A small Algonquian group living along the eastern shore of Lake Michigan, the Potawatomi were agriculturalists who, in the winter, spread out to hunt and trap in the great Michigan forests. Their healers were members of the Midewiwin society (see Ojibwa). Pushed inexorably westward, most Potawatomis live today in Oklahoma.

*SENECA.*   See Iroquois.

*SHOSHONE.*   The Shoshone were a hunting and gathering people of the Great Basin. With the introduction of horses, some Shoshone moved onto the plains as buffalo hunters, including the famous Comanche. Others continued their nomadic life in Basin, coming eventually into conflict with western ranchers. In this book, Shoshone refers to the Nevada Shoshone.

*TETON.*   The Teton were the largest of several branches of the great Dakota or Sioux tribe. Originally a woodland people of Minnesota whose staple food was wild rice, the Teton moved into the plains after obtaining horses, and became the definitive buffalo hunting tribe. After a half century of warfare with the United States Cavalry, the Teton were finally confined to five reservations in North and South Dakota in the late 19th century.

*TEWA.*   The Tewa are a linguistically related group of several Pueblo peoples from along the Rio Grande in New Mexico. Among the Tewa pueblos are San Ildefonso, San Juan and Santa Clara. The Tewa have a rich religious tradition and a complex ceremonial cycle. The magnificent black-on-black pottery of Maria Martinez and her San Ildefonso followers is world famous for its subtle beauty.

*THOMPSON INDIANS.*   The Thompson Indians, a Salishan tribe of southern British Columbia, were a riverine people who caught salmon in the great northwestern rivers and hunted the region's forests for deer, bear and caribou. Largely decimated by diseases introduced by gold miners in the 1860s, the tribe today occupies several British Columbia reserves.

*TLINGIT.* The Tlingit, living generally in what is now the southern Alaska panhandle near Sitka, exploited the rich fisheries and sea mammals of the Pacific coast. The Tlingit, makers of the great "totem poles" (actually grave markers), were superb craftsmen, unsurpassed in their abilities in woodworking.

*TSIMSHIAN.* A confederacy of three Northwest Coast groups (the Niska, Gitskan and Tsimshian-proper), the Tsimshian had an abundant food supply based on the exploitation of the sea and several great western rivers, the Nass and Skeena. Great craftsmen in wood like other Northwest Coast groups, Tsimshian women developed the intricate Chilkat robes woven of wool and cedar bark which displayed lineage totems and crests. In this book, Tsimshian refers to the "Tsimshian proper." See Gitskan.

*WASHOE,* The Washoe, a small hunting and gathering tribe, lived near the shores of Lake Tahoe. Gathered pine nuts were their most important food, supplemented by acorns, roots, berries and fish. Washoe culture was largely destroyed by the influx of thousands of gold miners in the 1860s.

*WINNEBAGO.* The Winnebago are a group who lived in the vicinity of Green Bay, Wisconsin. Practicing agriculture, hunting, gathering and fishing, the Winnebago were pushed west and largely dispersed by other Indian groups themselves forced west by Europeans. Winnebago women are famous for their beautiful applique sewing and other needlework.

*YOKUTS.* The Yokuts were a large California tribe living in the vicinity of the San Joachin valley and the foothills of the Sierra Nevada mountains. Fishing, hunting and gathering acorns and other nuts was the primary livelihood. Epidemics, gold rushes, and conflict with ranchers and farmers decimated this peaceful people so that today only a few hundred remain.

*ZUNI.* The Zuni are the largest of the southwestern Pueblo groups. Some 6,000 Zuni today live at their pueblo in New Mexico. The tribe has a generally theocratic culture. The people raise many varieties of corn as well as squash, beans, tobacco and other crops. Zuni silver jewelry is more detailed and delicate than the better known Navajo jewelry.

# Additional reading

## Medicinal plants

The published material on native American medicinal plants is generally quite technical, dispersed, and hard to find. Almost all of it is regional rather than national or continental in scope. Excellent material was often published in obscure scholarly or professional journals which can only be obtained today through inter-library loan offices of major research libraries. Several years ago, I gathered together a large portion of this material and abstracted the minimum requisite information from it, organized it, and published it in a book called *American Medical Ethnobotany: A Reference Dictionary* (New York, Garland Publishing Co., 1977). This is the most comprehensive available list of American medicinal plants describing 4,869 uses of 1,288 different species by 48 different cultures. The material is presented alphabetically by genus, by tribe, by family, and by use. It also contains an annotated bibliography of about 150 additional sources on the topic. It is, then, quite comprehensive. But it is also necessarily cryptic; while it is a useful reference book, it doesn't make very good reading!

Several books are available which describe the medicinal plants of individual native American groups. Frances Densmore's account of the ethnobotany of the Chippewa of Minnesota and Wisconsin, originally published by the Smithsonian Institution in 1927, has recently been reprinted as *How Indians Use Wild Plants for Food, Medicine, and Crafts* (New York, Dover, 1974). Huron H. Smith's classic volumes *Ethnobotany of the Ojibwe*, *Ethnobotany of the Forest Potawatomi*, *Ethnobotany of the Menominee*, and *Ethnobotany of the Meskwaki*, originally published in the early 1930s by the Public Museum of the City of Milwaukee, have all been reprinted recently. Erma Gunther's *Ethnobotany of Western Washington* (Revised Edition, Seattle, University of Washington Press, 1973) discusses a series of Northwest groups, among them the Nisqually,

Chinook, Skagit and Quileute. Paul Hamel and Mary Chiltoskey's *Cherokee Plants* (Sylva, N.C., Herald Publishing Co., 1975) is the only available summary on that important tribe.

Other material is less readily available. James Herrick's superb *Iroquois Medical Botany* is a doctoral dissertation available from University Microfilms in Ann Arbor, Michigan. Classic material on Navajo plant use by Paul Vestal, Clyde Kluckhohn and Leland Wyman is long out of print, and available only through large research libraries. The same is true of the monumental survey of Papago, Paiute and Shoshone medical plants by Train, Herricks and Archer.

To get detailed information on medicinal plants in your own region, the best thing to do is to consult your local librarian, or the nearest University library. Librarians, among the most helpful people in the world, can turn up the most unlikely things!

### American Indians

The published literature on American Indians is vast. Merwyn Garbarino's *Native American Heritage* (Boston, Little, Brown Co., 1976) provides a good non-technical overview. For a more complete and intensive account, see Robert Spencer and Jesse Jennings' *The Native Americans* (Second Edition, New York, Harper and Row, 1977). Either of these (and a host of similar books) will provide a useful guide to other books on individual Indian groups.

Virgil Vogel's *American Indian Medicine* (New York, Ballantine Books, 1970) is a good survey of the topic. Perhaps the best book from which to get a feeling for the interconnections of life, religion and medicine among native American peoples is Calvin Martin's *Keepers of the Game* (Berkeley, University of California Press, 1978). This extraordinary book — nominally a history of the fur trade in the northeastern United States and Canada — provides a compelling view of how people's action is structured and organized by their ideas of how the world works, and of the central position of notions of health among those ideas.

### Botany

There are any number of local or regional guides to plants, trees, flowers, mosses and so on. Best known are the ones in the Peterson

*Field Guide* series. Among the best of these is the *Field Guide to Rocky Mountain Wildflowers*, a lovely book no matter where you live.

There is no single account of the flora of North America. Although the Smithsonian Institution began a project to compile a **Flora North America,** somehow the funding for this magnificent project was cut off long before it was completed. The loss of this project — which would have been one of the great legacies of the twentieth century to all of our descendants — is, at best, terribly unfortunate.

There are excellent regional floras. For northeastern North America, Gray's *Manual of Botany* (first published in 1848 and now in its eighth edition, New York, Van Nostrand) is an extraordinary volume that provides detailed descriptions of over 6500 plant species. For the southeast, see Radford, et al., *Manual of the Vascular Flora of the Carolinas* (Chapel Hill, University of North Carolina Press, 1968); for the southwest, see Kearny and Peebles, *Arizona Flora* (Berkeley, University of California Press, 1970); for the far west, see Munz and Keck, *A California Flora* (Berkeley, University of California Press, 1970); for Alaska, see Hulten, *Flora of Alaska and Neighboring Territories* (Stanford, Stanford University Press, 1968).

\*　　\*　　\*

The following brief notes indicate some sources for specific topics discussed in various preceding chapters.

## INTRODUCTION.

The Cherokee Myth. James Mooney, *The Sacred Formulas of the Cherokees* (7th Annual Report of the Bureau of American Ethnology, 1885-1886. Smithsonian Institution, 1891).

On plants as medicines. Walter Lewis and Memory Elvin-Lewis, *Medical Botany: Plants Affecting Man's Health* (New York, John Wiley and Sons, 1977).

On meaningful medicines. Daniel E. Moerman, "The Anthropology of Symbolic Healing," *(Current Anthropology* 20:59-80, 1979).

## CULVER'S ROOT.

For some superb essays on early American medicine, see Richard H. Shryock, *Medicine in America: Historical Essays* (Baltimore, Johns Hopkins Press, 1966).

## MILKWEEDS, MONARCHS AND CENTAURS.

For a fascinating account of Monarch migrations, see Lincoln Brower's article "Monarch Migration" (*Natural History*, June/ July, 1977).

On the localization of toxins, see Brower and Glazier, "Localization of Heart Poisons in the Monarch Butterfly" (*Science* 188: 19-25, 1975).

On grosbeak and oriole predation on butterflies, see Fink and Brower, "Birds can overcome the cardenolide defense of Monarch butterflies in Mexico" *(Nature* 291:67-70, 1981).

## MISTLETOE.

For a superb, detailed and comprehensive account of mistletoe and other parasitic plants, see Job Kuijt's *The Biology of Parasitic Flowering Plants* (Berkeley, University of California Press, 1969).

## JIMSONWEED.

On hallucinogenic plants, see the monumental work by R.E. Schultes and A. Hofman, *Plants of the Gods, Origins of Hallucinogenic Use* (New York McGraw Hill, 1979). Also available is Schultes' much tinier but useful *Hallucinogenic Plants, A Golden Guide* (New York, Golden Press, 1976).

On European witch salves, see Michael Harner, *Hallucinogens and Shamanism* (New York, Oxford University Press, 1973).

## YARROW.

On the discovery and excavation of the Shanidar Neanderthals, see Ralph Solecki, *Shanidar, the First Flower People* (New York, Knopf, 1971).

Wild Geranium
(page 8)

Smooth Aster
(page 18)

Balsam Fir
(page 22)

Beard Tongue
(page 26)

Beebalm
(page 28)

Black Birch
(page 32)

Wintergreen
(page 32)

Bloodroot
(page 34)

Blue Flag
(page 38)

Burdock
(page 40)

Catnip
(page 44)

Chokecherry
(page 46)

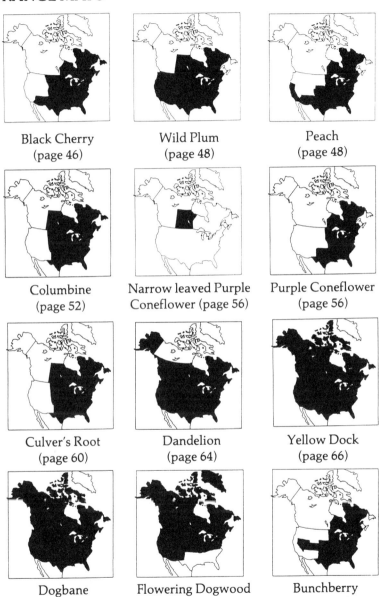

Black Cherry
(page 46)

Wild Plum
(page 48)

Peach
(page 48)

Columbine
(page 52)

Narrow leaved Purple
Coneflower (page 56)

Purple Coneflower
(page 56)

Culver's Root
(page 60)

Dandelion
(page 64)

Yellow Dock
(page 66)

Dogbane
(page 70)

Flowering Dogwood
(page 72)

Bunchberry
(page 72)

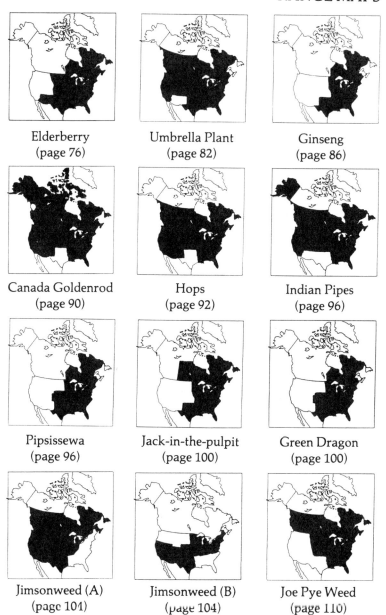

Elderberry
(page 76)

Umbrella Plant
(page 82)

Ginseng
(page 86)

Canada Goldenrod
(page 90)

Hops
(page 92)

Indian Pipes
(page 96)

Pipsissewa
(page 96)

Jack-in-the-pulpit
(page 100)

Green Dragon
(page 100)

Jimsonweed (A)
(page 104)

Jimsonweed (B)
(page 104)

Joe Pye Weed
(page 110)

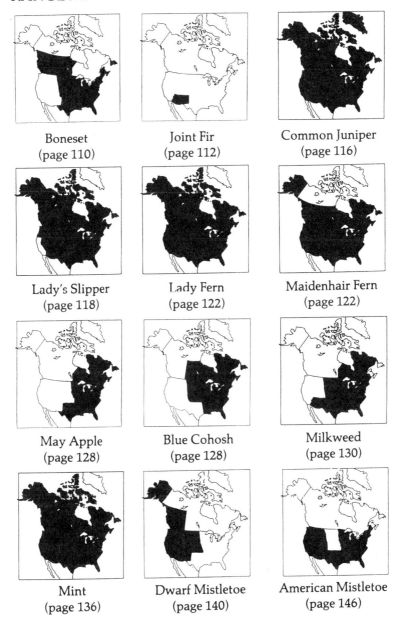

Boneset
(page 110)

Joint Fir
(page 112)

Common Juniper
(page 116)

Lady's Slipper
(page 118)

Lady Fern
(page 122)

Maidenhair Fern
(page 122)

May Apple
(page 128)

Blue Cohosh
(page 128)

Milkweed
(page 130)

Mint
(page 136)

Dwarf Mistletoe
(page 140)

American Mistletoe
(page 146)

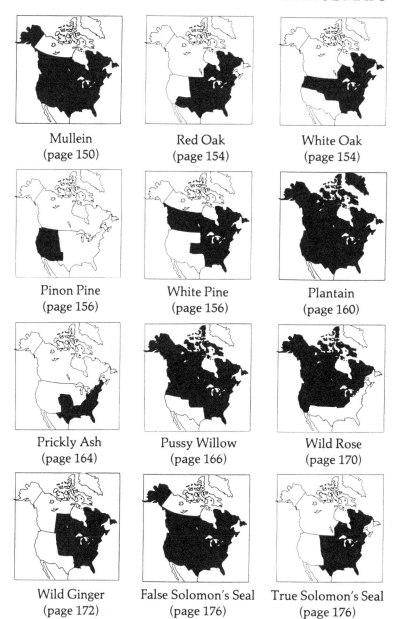

Mullein
(page 150)

Red Oak
(page 154)

White Oak
(page 154)

Pinon Pine
(page 156)

White Pine
(page 156)

Plantain
(page 160)

Prickly Ash
(page 164)

Pussy Willow
(page 166)

Wild Rose
(page 170)

Wild Ginger
(page 172)

False Solomon's Seal
(page 176)

True Solomon's Seal
(page 176)

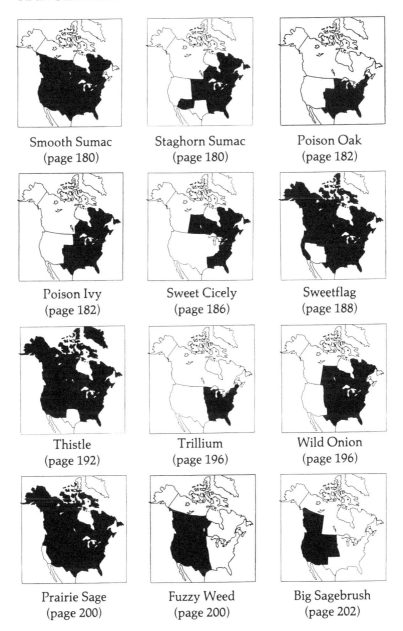

Smooth Sumac
(page 180)

Staghorn Sumac
(page 180)

Poison Oak
(page 182)

Poison Ivy
(page 182)

Sweet Cicely
(page 186)

Sweetflag
(page 188)

Thistle
(page 192)

Trillium
(page 196)

Wild Onion
(page 196)

Prairie Sage
(page 200)

Fuzzy Weed
(page 200)

Big Sagebrush
(page 202)

Western Mugwort
(page 202)

Absinthe
(page 204)

Tarragon
(page 204)

Yarrow
(page 206)

# Index

Illustrations are indicated in bold face type.